It's Another Ace Book from CGP

This book is for 8-9 year olds.

Classbooks 4A and 4B cover the shiny new Numeracy Strategy for year five at school.

They're brilliant fun. That makes them great classbooks — and fantastic books to use with kids at home.

Homework book 5 follows on from the classbooks with loads of extra-juicy questions to get brains bulging and marks rising.

CGP are just the best

The central aim of Coordination Group Publications is to produce top quality books that are carefully written, immaculately presented and marvellously funny — whilst always making sure they exactly cover the National Curriculum for each subject.

And then we supply them to as many people as we possibly can, as <u>cheaply</u> as we possibly can.

Buy our books — they're ace

Where to Find What

These Classbooks have been carefully tailored to exactly follow the order of teaching suggested in the National Numeracy Strategy for teaching maths. Of course, this means that each topic is split into bite-size units. To make it easier to find what you want, we've grouped them together here under the five main strands.

Solving Problems

Handling Data

Measures, Shape and Space

Published by Coordination Group Publications Ltd.

Co-edited by:
Glenn Rogers BSc (Hons) and Tim Wakeling BA(Hons)

Written and Illustrated by:
June Hall BSc (Hons) PhD
Mark Haslam BSc (Hons)
Simon Little BA (Hons)

Additional Writing and Illustrations by:
Charley Derbishire BA (Hons)
Gemma Hallam BA (Hons)
Laura Schibrowski BSc (Hons)

With thanks to Claire Thompson
for the Numeracy Strategy Research.

ISBN 1-84 146-054-0

Groovy website: www.cgpbooks.co.uk

Printed by Elanders Hindson, Newcastle upon Tyne.
Clipart sources: CorelDRAW and VECTOR.

Properties of Numbers

The Last Digit will tell you if it's Odd or Even

The last digit in the number 34 is 4.
4 is even, so 34 is even.

25 has a last digit of 5.
5 is odd, so 25 is odd.

34 is Even
25 is Odd

Are these numbers odd or even? Tick the correct box.

45   Even ☐   Odd ☑

54   Even ☐   Odd ☐

73   Even ☐   Odd ☐

84   Even ☐   Odd ☐

70   Even ☐   Odd ☐

26   Even ☐   Odd ☐

32   Even ☐   Odd ☐

89   Even ☐   Odd ☐

Only Even numbers can be divided exactly by 2.

Odd numbers can't.

Which of these numbers can be divided exactly by 2?

35 ☒   46 ☑   32 ☐

Just put a tick or a cross in the box.

29 ☐   14 ☐   99 ☐

Using the question above work out which of these are even:

35 ☒   46 ☑   32 ☐

29 ☐   14 ☐   99 ☐

Reasoning about Numbers

Finding Numbers that fit with Sums

Find a pair of numbers that add to make 11 and times together to make 30.

The <u>first thing</u> to do is find 2 numbers that <u>add up to 11</u>. I'll try 10 and 1. 10 + 1 = 11.
The next thing to do is to see if <u>10 and 1</u> times together to make 30:
<u>No</u>, 10 × 1 = 10. Crumbles.
Next I'll try <u>5 and 6</u>. They add up to make 11 and 5 × 6 = 30.

The pair of numbers are .... *5* and .... *6* .

Find a pair of numbers that add to make 11 and times together to make 24.

....

....

The pair of numbers are .... and ....

Put 3 different numbers in the 3 empty circles so that they add up to 15.

Again, put 3 different numbers in the 3 empty circles so that they add up to 15.

The great dragon of Ug has 3 ugly heads. Each head ate a different number of knights last Wednesday. Each head ate at least one knight, and they polished off 20 knights between them.

What is the greatest possible number of knights the left head could have eaten?

....

The greatest number the left head could have eaten is ....

Reasoning about Numbers

Find Examples to match Facts about Numbers

Marie says that if you add <u>three odd numbers</u> together, you get another <u>odd number</u>. Anna says that if that's true, she should be able to think of some <u>sums</u> with three odd numbers added together to give another odd number.

Help Marie out by writing down four sums that have three odd numbers added together to give another odd number.

....

....

$12 < \boxed{} < 15$

In this number statement, you could put <u>any number</u> between 12 and 15 in the box.

Write down three numbers that could go in the box.

They <u>don't</u> have to be <u>whole</u> numbers!

....

$0 < \boxed{} < 2$

In this number statement, you could put <u>any number</u> between 0 and 2 in the box.

Write down three numbers that could go in the box.

....

Larry is thinking about <u>multiples of 4</u>. All of the multiples of 4 that he can think of end with 0, 2, 4, 6, or 8.

Write down three more multiples of four.

....

Do any of them end with different numbers than 0, 2, 4, 6, or 8? ....

| Calculations | # *Understanding Multiplication* |

Multiplication is Repeated Addition

$$4 \times 7 = 7 + 7 + 7 + 7$$

Multiplication is just a short way of writing a long-winded addition sum.

Turn these addition sums into multiplications and then work them out.

4 + 4 + 4 + 4 + 4 = ...*5 × 4*...... = ...*20*......

5 + 5 + 5 + 5 + 5 = ... = ...

7 + 7 + 7 + 7 + 7 + 7 = ... = ...

9 + 9 + 9 + 9 + 9 + 9 + 9 + 9 + 9 = ... = ...

3 + 3 + 3 + 3 + 3 + 3 + 3 + 3 + 3 + 3 + 3 + 3 = ... = ...

Split Hard Multiplications into Easy Ones

I don't know my 13 times table, so if someone asked me to do 13 × 8, I would do 3 × 8 and then 10 × 8 and add the answers together.

3 + 10 = 13

Split these hard multiplications into easier ones and work out the answer.

13 × 8 = ...*3 × 8*... and ...*10 × 8*... = ...*24*... + ...*80*... = ...*104*...

15 × 6 = ... and .... = ... + ... = ...

14 × 7 = ... and .... = ... + ... = ...

23 × 5 = ... and .... = ... + ... = ...

Toni jumped over 8 school buses on her motortrike.
For safety reasons, each bus contained 35 juicy melons.

How many melons did she jump over?

35 × 8 = ... = ...

Understanding Division

Division is the Opposite of Multiplication

If you times 12 by 4 you get 48. $\quad 12 \times 4 = 48$
The opposite move is 48 divided by 4,
which gets you back to 12. $\quad 48 \div 4 = 12$

Write down a division sum that's opposite to each of these multiplications:

$7 \times 5 = 35$ means that $\underline{\;35\;} \div \underline{\;5\;} = \underline{\;7\;}$.

$6 \times 7 = 42$ means that $\underline{\;\;\;\;} \div \underline{\;\;\;\;} = \underline{\;\;\;\;}$.

$13 \times 4 = 52$ means that $\underline{\;\;\;\;} \div \underline{\;\;\;\;} = \underline{\;\;\;\;}$.

Write down 2 division sums that are opposite to each of these multiplications:

$15 \times 9 = 135$ means that $\underline{\;135\;} \div \underline{\;15\;} = \underline{\;9\;}$ and $\underline{\;135\;} \div \underline{\;9\;} = \underline{\;15\;}$.

$7 \times 11 = 77$ means that $\underline{\;\;\;\;} \div \underline{\;\;\;\;} = \underline{\;\;\;\;}$ and $\underline{\;\;\;\;} \div \underline{\;\;\;\;} = \underline{\;\;\;\;}$.

$8 \times 9 = 72$ means that $\underline{\;\;\;\;} \div \underline{\;\;\;\;} = \underline{\;\;\;\;}$ and $\underline{\;\;\;\;} \div \underline{\;\;\;\;} = \underline{\;\;\;\;}$.

If you know one sum, then you should be able to write
down the other two as well — without working them out.

During the Tomato Cricket Tournament, **24** overs were bowled
in each match. **6** tomatoes were bowled in each over.

Work out how many tomatoes were bowled in the match.

$24 \times 6 = \underline{\;\;\;\;}$

Now write down one sum that tells you how many
overs were bowled, and another sum that tells you
how many tomatoes were bowled in an over.

$\underline{\;\;\;\;} \div \underline{\;6\;} = \underline{\;\;\;\;}$ and $\underline{\;\;\;\;} \div \underline{\;24\;} = \underline{\;\;\;\;}$

The Great Divide — don't let it bowl you over...

Division is the opposite of multiplication. So, if you know a multiplication sum, you
know <u>two</u> division sums as well. Hmmm, that sounds like a pretty good deal to me...

Division with Remainders

Sometimes You Can't Divide Exactly

Try doing $10 \div 4$ and you'll notice that it's a bit tricky. 4 only goes into 10 twice ($4 \times 2 = 8$), with 2 left over. The bit left over is called the remainder.

Which of these divisions can you do exactly? Tick the ones that you can.

$45 \div 9$ ☑
Yes, the answer is 5.

$26 \div 4$ ☒
No, the answer is 6 remainder 2.

$56 \div 7$ ☐

$25 \div 7$ ☐

$24 \div 9$ ☐

$24 \div 3$ ☐

Work out these division sums and write down the remainder.

$15 \div 7 =$ ......2...... with remainder ......1......

$13 \div 6 =$ .... with remainder ....

$12 \div 5 =$ .... with remainder ....

$34 \div 8 =$ .... with remainder ....

In certain villages of England it is illegal to crush nuts with a phone*.

I have 35 nuts and 6 phones. If I crush the same number of nuts with each phone, how many nuts will I have left over?

Throw away the key.

$35 \div 6 =$ ....

There are .... nuts left over.

Let that be a lesson to y'all

* Completely made up nonsense.

Division with Remainders

Remainders can be Written in Different Ways

There are lots of ways to write the remainder. Here are a few of them:

$14 \div 4 = 3$ remainder 2

$14 \div 4 = 3$ rem 2

$14 \div 4 = 3$ r 2

Or for the really keen,

$14 = 4 \times 3 + 2$

These all mean the same thing.

Work out these division sums and write down the remainders.

$23 \div 7 =$ ......3...... remainder ....2....

$17 \div 5 =$ .... remainder ....

$25 \div 7 =$ .... remainder ....

$43 \div 6 =$ .... remainder ....

$29 \div 7 =$ .... rem ....

$11 \div 2 =$ .... rem ....

$64 \div 6 =$ .... r ....

$84 \div 9 =$ .... r ....

Bernard has made 37 spam and cream sandwiches. He is going to put them all into sandwich bags. Each bag holds 4 sandwiches. How many bags does he need?

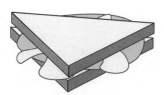

Bernard needs .... sandwich bags.

Don't forget — all the sandwiches need to go in bags — including the remainder.

Ace Space Pens cost £2. Sally has £7 to spend on new pens. How many Ace Space Pens can she buy?

Sally can buy .... Ace Space Pens.

Sally can only buy a whole number of pens.

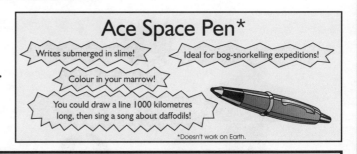

Ace Space Pen*

Writes submerged in slime!

Ideal for bog-snorkelling expeditions!

Colour in your marrow!

You could draw a line 1000 kilometres long, then sing a song about daffodils!

*Doesn't work on Earth.

If you forget this — you need a remainder reminder...

The remainder is just what's <u>left over</u> when you do a division. When you can't take away any more of the number you're dividing by, what's left is the <u>remainder</u>.

Calculations — Division Using Your Times Tables

To do Divisions Quickly
You need to Know your Times Tables

Using your times tables, do these divisions as quickly as you can:

14 ÷ 2 = ...*7*... because ...*7*... × ...*2*... = ...*14*...

18 ÷ 3 = ... because .... × .... = ...

24 ÷ 4 = ... because .... × .... = ...

35 ÷ 5 = ... because .... × .... = ...

60 ÷ 10 = ... because .... × .... = ...

Now see how quickly you can do these:

8 ÷ 2 = ...   20 ÷ 2 = ...   16 ÷ 2 = ...

9 ÷ 3 = ...   21 ÷ 3 = ...   12 ÷ 3 = ...

8 ÷ 4 = ...   32 ÷ 4 = ...   16 ÷ 4 = ...

15 ÷ 5 = ...   25 ÷ 5 = ...   40 ÷ 5 = ...

20 ÷ 10 = ...   80 ÷ 10 = ...   50 ÷ 10 = ...

Mark's favourite hobby is to sit on the beach and watch the world go by.

He has 36 sticks of chewing gum left to last him the next 4 days.

How many sticks of chewing gum can he have each day, if he shares them out equally?

36 ÷ 4 = ...

because .... × .... = ...

Division Using Your Times Tables

6, 7, 8 and 9 Times Tables are a Bit Harder

Using your times tables, do these divisions as quickly as you can:

28 ÷ 7 = ...*4*.... because ...*4*... × ...*7*... = ...*28*... .

42 ÷ 6 = ... because .... × .... = ...

40 ÷ 8 = ... because .... × .... = ...

72 ÷ 9 = ... because .... × .... = ...

It's OK if you have to think for a bit with these.

Now here's some more. Think about your times tables to do them.

48 ÷ 6 = ...   30 ÷ 6 = ...   54 ÷ 6 = ...

49 ÷ 7 = ...   42 ÷ 7 = ...   77 ÷ 7 = ...

56 ÷ 8 = ...   32 ÷ 8 = ...   72 ÷ 8 = ...

45 ÷ 9 = ...   63 ÷ 9 = ...   54 ÷ 9 = ...

Lucy has 54 lollipop-sucking goldfish. How many fish tanks will she need if she puts 6 goldfish in each tank?

54 ÷ 6 = ...

because .... × .... = ...

Ben counts 64 chocolate raisins in a packet of Pullworth's Chocolate Raisins. He decides to share them out between his eight ferrets. How many raisins will each ferret get?

64 ÷ 8 = ...

because .... × .... = ...

Calculations	*__Multiplying Tricks__*

Multiplying a number by 9 is easy.
Multiply by 10, then take the number away.

What is 35 × 9?

Well, 35 × 9 will be <u>35 less than 35 × 10</u>.
35 × 10 = 350 (just add a zero to the 35)
So 35 × 9 = 350 − 35 = <u>315</u>.

For public safety reasons, Mad Ram McGnasher is kept in a reinforced steel barn.
Last year he destroyed 9 lightweight barns, at a cost of £56 each.

Calculate 9 × £56 by working out 10 × £56.

10 × £56 = ..., so 9 × £56 = ... − .... = ...

Now see if you can work out these in your head:

32 × 9 = ...   22 × 9 = ...   39 × 9 = ...

89 × 9 = ...   37 × 9 = ...   42 × 9 = ...

What is 35 × 11?   35 × 11 will be <u>35 more than 35 × 10</u>.
35 × 10 = 350, so 35 × 11 = 350 + 35 = <u>385</u>.

Froggatt's Sprout Cookies aren't selling too well.
Mr Froggatt wonders if they might be too expensive at £26 a biscuit.
How much does a pack of 11 biscuits cost?

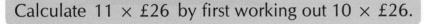

Calculate 11 × £26 by first working out 10 × £26.

10 × £26 = ..., so 11 × £26 = ... + ... = ...

See if you can do these sums in your head:

32 × 11 = ...   22 × 11 = ...   39 × 11 = ...

89 × 11 = ...   37 × 11 = ...   42 × 11 = ...

Multiplying On Paper

Split Multiplications into Tens and Units

If you get multiplication sums with big numbers, just split them up.
— They're much easier if you do the tens and units separately.

It's always a good idea to do an approximation —
then you know if your answer's more or less right.

EXAMPLE: 52×7

approximately 50×10

Pick nice easy
numbers that are
close to the ones
in the question.

```
    52
 ×   7
  350  ←←←  50 × 7
 +  14  ←  2 × 7
  364
```

① Split the bigger number
into tens and units.
Multiply them separately.

② Add the two
multiplications together.

$50 \times 10 = \underline{500}$, so the answer
should be of a similar size to 500.
If you worked it out to be 3000,
you'd know it was wrong.

Once you get used to that, you can start doing them like this...

①
Work out 2×7 first.

②
$2 \times 7 = 14$. Write the 4 here as
normal, but put the 1 underneath.

We say the 1 has been carried.

```
   52
 ×  7
    4
   1
```

③ Now do 5×7, but
add on the carried 1.

④ $5 \times 7 = 35$.
Adding the 1 gives 36.

That's it. The answer's 364.

```
   52
 ×  7
  364
   1
```

Do these by splitting into tens and units and multiplying separately.

$$\begin{array}{r} 38 \\ \times \ 5 \\ \hline \end{array} \qquad \begin{array}{r} 91 \\ \times \ 3 \\ \hline \end{array} \qquad \begin{array}{r} 73 \\ \times \ 4 \\ \hline \end{array}$$

Do these by multiplying the units first and carrying over.

$$\begin{array}{r} 56 \\ \times \ 6 \\ \hline \end{array} \qquad \begin{array}{r} 24 \\ \times \ 7 \\ \hline \end{array} \qquad \begin{array}{r} 49 \\ \times \ 3 \\ \hline \end{array}$$

Mult iplic ations — split them up to make life easier...

Don't worry if it takes a while to get the hang of this. Take it slowly and keep practising.
Look through the method and check you understand it before you try the questions.

Real Life Problems

Brian had 129 bars of soap in his pocket. He then found 47 more bars in his left ear. He was a bit grubby, so he had a bath and used 42 bars of soap. How many bars of soap did he have left?

129 bars of soap + 47 bars of soap = ... bars of soap.

.... bars of soap – 42 bars of soap = ... bars of soap.

So he had .... bars of soap left.

There were 143 tins of green paint on the painting table in the bat cave. There were 32 tins of blue paint on the table. The bats knocked 84 tins off the table while flapping around at night. How many tins of paint were left?

So there were .... tins of paint left on the table.

Kelly had 98 giant paper clips to share with her sister Shelly. Then she bought a brand new box of 50 giant paper clips. If Kelly shares out all the paper clips, how many will she and Shelly have each?

98 + 50 = ...

.... ÷ 2 = ..., so they will each have .... giant paperclips.

There are 32 children in Mrs Feeblebunny's class. Half of them walk to school in the morning, and one quarter of them catch the school bus. How many children get to school another way?

Watch out for that hoverboard, Mum!

....

....

Put your working out on these two lines.

.... children go to school another way.

Real Life Problems

Jerry had 5 piles of his famous exploding "Spam Kerbam Jam". He had three piles with 15 jars each and two piles with 3 jars each. How many jars did he have altogether?

3 × 15 = ..., 2 × 3 = ...

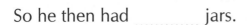

.... + ... = ..., so he had .... jars.

A few days later 15 of the jars exploded, but luckily Jerry had made 24 more jars. How many jars did he then have?

....

So he then had .... jars.

Penelope likes to bathe in cabbage juice before going out for the evening. Last January she had 120 bottles, but by the end of May she had used half of them. She now has only a third of what she had at the end of May. How many bottles of cabbage juice does she have left?

120 bottles ÷ 2 = ... bottles at the end of May.

.... bottles ÷ 3 = ... bottles of cabbage juice left.

There are 36 flasks hidden behind Professor Rumdunker's desk. Half of them contain red liquid. A third of them contain green liquid. The rest are empty.

How many of the Professor's flasks contain liquid?

....

....

So .... flasks contain liquid.

Real Life Problems? What — you mean like school...

With these problems you have to decide <u>which sum</u> to do. If you've used <u>all</u> the numbers in the question and the answer <u>sounds</u> about right, you've probably got it right.

Number Stories

These 2 pages are cool — you get to <u>make stuff up</u>.

Number Stories <u>with</u> _+ and –_

Make a number story from this sum: 43 + 234 = 277.

My brother Rex has 43 mouldy potatoes in his room. I have 234 in mine. Together we have a total of 277 mouldy potatoes.

Together means +

Now you have a go at making up your <u>own</u> story. You can use the one above as a guide — just <u>change</u> the <u>numbers</u> and the "<u>mouldy potatoes</u>" bits.

Make a number story from this sum: 23 + 532 = 555.

....

....

....

Make a number story from this sum: 54 + 235 = 289.

Try to think of <u>a story that ends</u> "Altogether <u>289</u> <u>snowmen</u> climbed the <u>giant green lampshade</u>."

Don't make it a long story!

....

....

....

Make a number story from this sum: 557 – 44 = 513.

Watch it — there is a <u>minus</u> in this one.
Try <u>starting</u> your number story with <u>557 things</u> and then <u>losing 44</u> of them...

....

....

....

Number Stories

Number Stories with × and ÷

Make a number story from this sum: 4 × 12 = 48.

I have 4 packets of Froggatt's Mouldy Mouse Crackers. Each packet contains 12 crackers. Altogether I have 48 Mouldy Mouse Crackers.

Think of 4 × 12 as 4 lots of 12. Then all you have to do is think of a number story to go with it.

Make a number story from this sum: 8 × 14 = 112.

Use the number story in the box, but remember to change the numbers. And turn the bits about "Froggatt's Mouldy Mouse Crackers" into something exciting.

....

....

....

Make a number story from this sum: 12 × 12 = 144.

How about putting 12 French dancing bees somewhere in your number story?

....

....

....

Make a number story from this sum: 244 ÷ 4 = 61.

This one is a division. Have a go at sharing between 4 friends.

....

....

....

NUMBer stories — tales about pins and needles?...

Try to keep your stories short — you don't need to think up long ones. All that really matters is that the story matches the sum. If it does that, then it must be right.

Numbers and the Number System

Fractions and Decimals

Finding a Fraction is just about Dividing

Work these out by dividing:

$\frac{1}{5}$ of 35 = ...*35*... ÷ ...*5*... = ...

> So long as there is a <u>1 on top</u> of the fraction, you can just <u>divide</u> by the <u>bottom</u> number.

$\frac{1}{5}$ of 50 = ... ÷ .... = ...

$\frac{1}{4}$ of 28 = ... ÷ .... = ...

$\frac{1}{4}$ of 16 = ... ÷ .... = ...

$\frac{1}{4}$ of 40 = ... ÷ .... = ...

Converting to Decimals

> To work out a fraction of 1 pound, 1 metre, or any <u>1 thing</u>, just write the <u>fraction</u> as a <u>decimal</u>.

Work out these fractions of £1.

$\frac{1}{5}$ of £1 = ...*£0.20*...

> **You need to know what these <u>fractions</u> are as <u>decimals</u> —**
> $\frac{1}{4}$ = 0.25, $\frac{1}{5}$ = 0.2, $\frac{1}{10}$ = 0.1.

$\frac{1}{4}$ of £1 = ...

$\frac{1}{10}$ of £1 = ...

Write down these fractions of 1 m.

$\frac{1}{10}$ of 1 m = ... m

$\frac{1}{4}$ of 1 m = ... m

$\frac{1}{5}$ of 1 m = ... m

Arnold has 20 kg of pond slime. He wants to give $\frac{1}{4}$ of it to each of his 4 nephews. How much does each nephew get?

$\frac{1}{4}$ of 20 kg = ... ÷ .... = ... kg

If Arnold shares another 20 kg of slime between his 5 brothers, how much do each of them get?

.... of 20 kg = ... kg

Fractions — they're NOT A WHOLE load of fun...

Decimals and fractions are just two different ways of writing the same numbers. Some fractions come up a lot, like $\frac{1}{2}$, $\frac{1}{4}$, $\frac{1}{5}$ and $\frac{1}{10}$, so it's a good idea to learn them as decimals.

Fractions and Decimals

Turn these into Fractions

That's strange, 10p looks bigger than a pound to me...

What fraction of £1 is 10p?

Just write down how many ten pences make a pound, then put 1 over that number.

.... 10p coins make £1, so 10p is .... of £1.

What fraction of 1 m is 25 cm?

Don't forget — there are 100 cm in 1 m, so you can divide 25 cm into 100 cm.

There are .... lots of 25 cm in 1 m, so 25 cm is .... of 1m.

What fraction of the large shape is each of these small shapes?

The small shape has .... squares.   Write this number

The large shape has .... squares.   over this number

The small shape is .... the size of the large shape.   to give this fraction.

The small shape has .... squares.

The small shape is .... the size of the large shape.

Fill in this table, writing the small weight as a fraction of the big weight.

Just write the small weight over the big weight — the first answer is $\frac{1}{2}$.

Small Weight	Big Weight	Fraction
1 kg	2 kg	....
1 kg	5 kg	....
1 kg	4 kg	....
3 kg	4 kg	....

Fractions and Decimals

Putting a Pair of Decimals in Order

If you need to work out which number is <u>biggest</u>, use this <u>3-step method</u> — but make sure you do the steps <u>in order</u>.

1) Check if one number has <u>more digits</u> to the <u>left</u> of the <u>decimal point</u>.

2) <u>If not</u>, look at the first digits of the numbers. Check which is bigger.

3) If they both have the same first digit, <u>check the next digit</u>.

52.0 is bigger than **5.2**

6.4 is bigger than **2.4**

4.63 is bigger than **4.36**

Which of these is bigger?

10 cm or 1.0 cm? .... cm

8.2 kg or 6.9 kg? ....kg

5.05 m or 5.50 m? ....m

Putting a List of Decimals in Order

Put the numbers 2.5, 3.5, 6.7, 9.2 and 1.7 in order, with the smallest number first.

It's a good idea to jot down a <u>number line</u> — that way you can see <u>exactly</u> where the numbers go.

Make sure you check if you're asked for the <u>smallest first</u> or <u>largest first</u>.

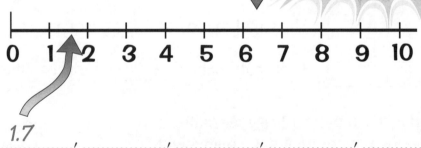

1.7

................,/ ....,/ ....,/ ....,/ ....

Put £9, 99p, £1.99, 90p and £9.01 in order, largest first.

First write all the amounts in pence:

................,/ ....,/ ....,/ ....,/ ....

It's easier to see which is largest when they're all in <u>pence</u>.

Now put the amounts in order:

................,/ ....,/ ....,/ ....,/ ....

Fractions and Decimals

Writing Tenths as Decimals

EXAMPLE: Write fifty-seven and nine tenths as a decimal.

Just treat the "and" as the decimal point — write down the <u>whole number</u>, then a decimal point, then the <u>number of tenths</u>. Easy.

So the answer is
57.9

Write these numbers as decimals:

Three and one tenth = ...

Nine and three tenths = ...

Twenty-two and six tenths = ...

Eighteen and four tenths = ...

Sixty-five and five tenths = ...

Forty-eight and two tenths = ...

What are these fractions as decimals?

$\frac{1}{2}$ = ... $\frac{1}{4}$ = ... $\frac{3}{4}$ = ...

Veronica has a jar of Gourmet Beetroot Paste to share with her 3 friends. What fraction will they each get?   ....

How much is that as a decimal?   ....

Veronica also has a pot of parsnip flavoured yoghurt which she shares with her best friend Gillian. What fraction do they have each?

....

How much is that as a decimal?   ....

Tenths — Don't you buy then in camping shops?...

Writing tenths as decimals isn't too hard — because you don't have to work anything out. You just have to get the number of tenths in the right place after the decimal point.

Venn Diagrams

Venn Diagrams *show the groups things are in*

This diagram splits up even numbers and numbers over 30. Using the diagram, write down:

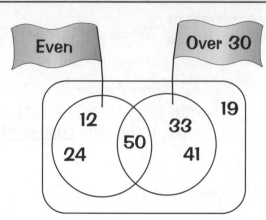

the even numbers: ...., ..., ...

the numbers over 30: ...., ..., ...

the even numbers over 30: ....

the numbers that are not even and not over 30: ....

Fill in this Venn diagram with odd numbers and numbers under 10.

Make sure that anything <u>in both circles</u> is odd <u>and</u> under 10.

Pick 2 odd numbers that <u>are under 10</u> and 2 that <u>are not</u> under 10.

The numbers <u>outside</u> the 2 circles <u>can't</u> be odd <u>or</u> under 10.

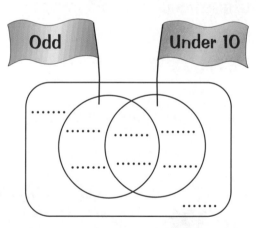

Choose 2 other types of numbers and then put them on this diagram.

Don't use something like "numbers over 20" <u>and</u> "numbers under 20" or there <u>won't</u> be any overlap.

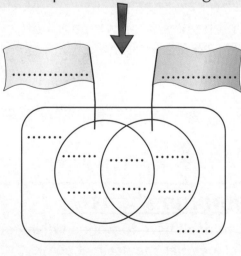

If you <u>really can't</u> think of anything yourself, try using <u>"numbers in the 3 times table"</u> for one of them.

Carroll Diagrams

Carroll Diagrams — groups in columns and rows

Here's how it works: One row is filled with numbers that follow a <u>rule</u> — for example being <u>even</u>, or <u>over 10</u>. The other row has numbers that <u>don't</u> follow the rule. It's the same with the columns. If a number is in the "<u>evens</u>" row <u>and</u> in the "<u>not over 10</u>" column, it's a number that's <u>both</u> even <u>and</u> not over 10, like 4 or 6.

Look at this Carroll diagram. Some of the numbers are odd, some are over 20, some are both and some are neither. Which are which?

If something's <u>crossed out</u>, just read "<u>not</u>" before it.

	Over 20	~~Over 20~~
Odd Numbers	21 55	3 19
~~**Odd Numbers**~~	22 30	6 18

odd numbers: ...., ..., ..., ...

Don't forget to count odd numbers over 20 <u>and</u> odd numbers not over 20.

These are the <u>even</u> numbers <u>not</u> over 20.

numbers that are not odd: ...., ..., ..., ...

numbers over 20: ...., ..., ..., ...

numbers over 20 that are not odd: ...., ...   odd numbers over 20: ...., ...

Put the numbers 3, 12, 15, 16 and 25 in the right places on this diagram.

Choose 2 types of number, then fill in this diagram:

	3 × Table	~~3 × Table~~
Even Numbers	....	....
~~**Even Numbers**~~	....	....

	....	~~........~~
....	....	....
~~........~~	....	....

Not that kind of carol...

Remember the spelling — "Car-roll diagram"...

If you're drawing a Venn diagram or a Carroll diagram, always make sure your <u>labels</u> are clear. If they're not, no one will be able to read it.

Numbers and the Number System	*Ordering Numbers*

"<" Is a Quick Way to Write Less Than

So wherever you see the "<" symbol, just read it as "less than".

Write down a number which is < 213.

So "< 213" just means "less than 213".

....

Find a number so that 47 < your number.

This time, 47 needs to be less than your number — in other words, find a number bigger than 47.

....

Pick a number with 47 < your number < 213.

Now your number needs to be between the 2 numbers — check if the numbers you've used already work.

....

Find 3 numbers between 5346 and 5646.

5346 < .... < 5646

5346 < .... < 5646

5346 < .... < 5646

5346 5646

I said numbers — not numbskulls.

Use ">" Instead of "Bigger than"

Find all the numbers between 7230 and 7234.

7234 > .... > 7230

7234 > .... > 7230   7234 > .... > 7230

Use "=" to Say "the Same as"

Mavis Miggins lassoed 4672 donkeys in a freak knitting accident. Last year she tied together 4692 armadillos and 4672 cows.

Fill in the gaps with a <, > or = symbol.

4672 4692   4692 4672   4672 4672

Rounding Numbers

Rounding to the Nearest 10 or 100

Round these to the nearest 10.

23 = ... (to nearest 10)

47 = ... (to nearest 10)

65 = ... (to nearest 10)

> Just look at the <u>last digit</u> — if it's 1, 2, 3 or 4 round down, if it's <u>5 or more</u> round up.

18 = ... (to nearest 10)

121 = ... (to nearest 10)

Round these to the nearest 100.   230 = *200* (to nearest 100)

> This time look at the <u>last 2 digits</u> — if they are <u>50 or more</u> round up, otherwise round down.

124 = ... (to nearest 100)

660 = ... (to nearest 100)

450 = ... (to nearest 100)

Rounding Makes Sums Easier

Underline the best approximation for 608 + 493:

600 + 500   600 + 400

610 + 93   68 + 500

> Look for the sum that has the number closest to 608 <u>and</u> the number closest to 493.

> Just round <u>both</u> numbers to the nearest 10 <u>then</u> multiply them together — it's a doddle.

Harvey thought he was supposed to wear a shirt and tyre to job interviews. He has failed 19 interviews on each of the last 11 days. Approximately how many interviews has he failed in total?

.... × .... = ...

It's ROUND about the end of the page...

You use rounding when you don't need to get an exact answer. It makes sums easier. The main thing to remember is — If the number is <u>halfway</u>, you round <u>up</u>.

Numbers and the Number System

Estimating Whole Numbers

Estimate Amounts by Multiplying

Estimate the number of marrows Steve is juggling:

approximate number per row = ...

approximate number of rows = ...

.... × .... = ... marrows

Harry buys 5 cans of Froggatt's Garlic Juice. Each one contains the juice of about 50 garlic bulbs. Estimate how many bulbs were used to make Harry's drinks.

.... × .... = ... bulbs

Unmarked Number Lines

Estimate the positions of the marks on these number lines.

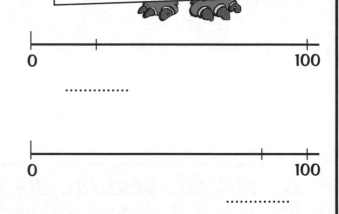

It might help to put in some extra points of your own — 50 halfway along, 25 a quarter of the way...

0   100

....

0   100

....

0   100

....

0   100

....

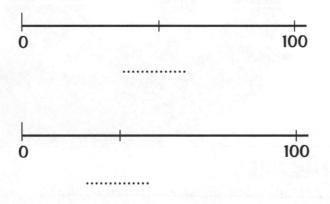

Estimating Proportions

Half Full or Half Empty

There were 30 chocolates in this box when it was full. Estimate how many are left.

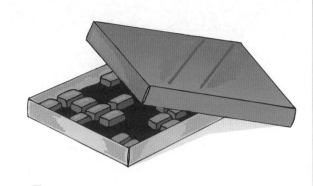

I'd say the box is about <u>half</u> full — so just <u>divide</u> 30 by 2.

.... ÷ .... = ...

This vial held 200 marbles when it was full. Unfortunately some have been stolen by the evil Baron Gargleflump. Estimate how many marbles are left.

....

How Many More Times...

The glass on the left has more cauliflower juice. Estimate how much fuller it is than the glass on the right.

Just look <u>how high up</u> the glass each drink goes — then say if it's the same, twice as far or somewhere <u>in between</u>.

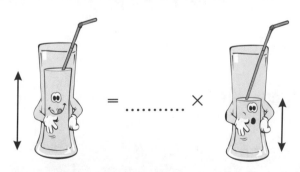

= .... ×

So it's .... times as full.

How much more milk does Roger have?

Don't forget — just look at the <u>heights</u>.

= .... ×

So Roger has .... times as much milk.

Reading Scales

Measure Lengths in Centimetres and Metres

Write down the measurement marked on each of these rulers.

mm
120 130 140 150

mm
170 180 190 20

mm
90 100 110 120

........137........ mm

.... mm

.... mm

What are these measurements in centimetres?

Don't forget — there are 100 cm in 1 m.

.......13.7........ cm

.... cm

.... cm

Now convert your measurements into centimetres and millimetres.

.....13.... cm ...7.... mm

.... cm .... mm

.... cm .... mm

Remember — it's in cm, not mm.

110 120 130 140 150 160 170 1

How tall is Billy in centimetres?

.... cm

How tall is Billy in metres?

.... m

What is that in metres and centimetres?

.... m .... cm

Use a ruler to measure the length of your hand.
Write down the measurement in metres and centimetres:

.... m .... cm

and just in metres:

.... m

Reading scales? Sounds a bit fishy to me...

Reading scales isn't hard when you know <u>how</u>. Always make sure you know
how big each of the <u>divisions</u> is — then all you have to do is <u>count</u> them up.

Reading Scales

Rounding Numbers

Read the scales on these measuring cylinders. How much slime do they contain, to the nearest 10 ml?

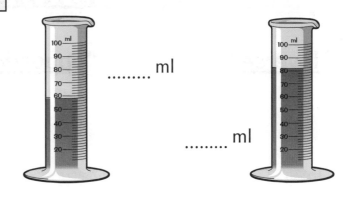

.... ml

.... ml

Round these lengths to the nearest 100 cm.

380 cm = ... cm (to the nearest 100 cm)

220 cm = ... cm (to the nearest 100 cm)

590 cm = ... cm (to the nearest 100 cm)

150 cm = ... cm (to the nearest 100 cm)

Don't let the <u>units</u> fool you, just think about the <u>numbers</u>. Remember — if it ends in <u>50</u> <u>or more</u>, round it <u>up</u>.

Round all these to the nearest 10 ml and the nearest 100 ml.

129 ml = ... ml (to the nearest 10 ml) — or .... ml (to the nearest 100 ml).

783 ml = ... ml (to the nearest 10 ml) — or .... ml (to the nearest 100 ml).

566 ml = ... ml (to the nearest 10 ml) — or .... ml (to the nearest 100 ml).

345 ml = ... ml (to the nearest 10 ml) — or .... ml (to the nearest 100 ml).

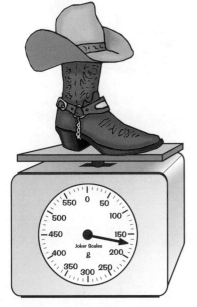

Mariella McGee is a bit short. How heavy is she? .... g

How much is that to the nearest 100 g?

Have a look on the <u>dial</u> to see which it's <u>closest</u> to — 100 g or 200 g.

.... g

How much is 250 g to the nearest 100 g? .... g

Understanding + and –

Subtraction is the Inverse of Addition

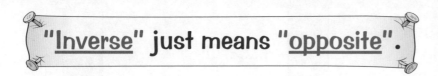

"Inverse" just means "opposite".

So if you add something on, <u>then</u> take it away again, you <u>get back</u> to the number you <u>started with</u>.

Write down the inverse of each of these.

The inverse of "add 47" is *subtract 47* .

The inverse of "add 28" is ....

The inverse of "add 15" is ....

Just change "<u>add</u>" to "<u>subtract</u>" — couldn't be simpler.

Pick a number to add on, then do the inverse.

You can pick <u>any</u> number here, but I'd pick something that's <u>easy to add on</u>.

35 + *42* = *77* so *77* – *42* = *35*

64 + ... = ... so .... – .... = ...

21 + ... = ... so .... – .... = ...

Add a number to the front, then do the inverse.

10 + 56 = *66* so *66* – *10* = *56*

.... + 11 = ... so .... – .... = ...

.... + 72 = ... so .... – .... = ...

Remember, the <u>order</u> doesn't matter with addition — so 10+56 is <u>the same</u> as 56+10.

Gordon has an impressive collection of fancy dress costumes. He has 25 authentic historical costumes and 72 others. How many costumes does Gordon have in total?

.... + ... = ...

Now check your answer by doing the inverse.

<u>Take 25</u> from the answer to get <u>back to 72</u> — or <u>take 72</u> away to get <u>back to 25</u>.

.... – .... = ...

Understanding + and –

Addition is the Inverse of Subtraction

If you <u>take</u> any number <u>away</u>, and then <u>add it back on</u>, you're back to the number you <u>started</u> with — magic.

Write down the inverse of each of these.

Just change the "<u>subtract</u>" to an "<u>add</u>" — but keep the numbers the same.

The inverse of "subtract 12" is ....

The inverse of "subtract 102" is

....

The inverse of "subtract 438" is

....

Fill in the inverse of these subtractions.

The inverse of $115 - 13 =$ ...*102*... is ...*102*... + ...*13*... = 115.

The inverse of $679 - 531 =$ .... is .... + ... = 679.

The inverse of $536 - 221 =$ .... is .... + ... = 536.

The inverse of $868 - 835 =$ .... is .... + ... = 868.

It doesn't really matter which way round you write the addition — 102+13 is <u>the same as</u> 13+102.

Underline the inverse of $492 - 381 = 111$:

$492 + 381 = 111$ $111 - 381 = 492$

$111 + 381 = 492$ $249 + 381 = 111$

You're looking for the <u>inverse</u> of a subtraction — so the answer must be an addition.

Johnnie is playing a card game. So far he has a score of 214 and his friend Jimmy has scored 256. How far is Johnnie behind?

Addition is the <u>inverse</u> of subtraction — that means you can <u>check</u> your subtraction with an addition.

....

Check your subtraction with an addition:

....

Calculations	# Mental Strategies

Order Doesn't Matter in Addition

Pair up the additions that give the same answer.

53 + 27   68 + 169

169 + 68   898 + 989   22 + 147   989 + 898

27 + 53   147 + 22

Just find **2** sums with the <u>same</u> <u>numbers</u> — don't worry about the order, it doesn't matter.

Find 2 sums to go with each answer.

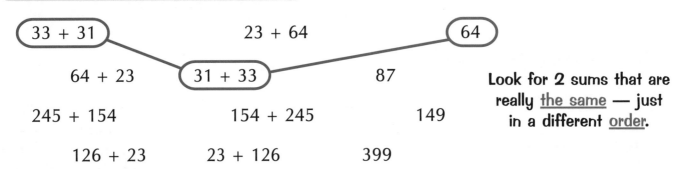

33 + 31   23 + 64   64

64 + 23   31 + 33   87

245 + 154   154 + 245   149

126 + 23   23 + 126   399

Look for **2** sums that are really <u>the same</u> — just in a different <u>order</u>.

Pick out 4 sums which are related.

37 + 79 = 116

73 + 97 = 116

Use these <u>2 important facts</u>:
1) <u>Order</u> doesn't matter for addition.
2) Addition and subtraction are <u>inverses</u>.

79 + 37 = 116

179 – 37 = 79   116 – 79 = 37

116 – 37 = 79   37 – 79 = 116

Use 56 + 88 = 144 to find the answer to:

Just see which number's <u>missing</u> — and that's your <u>answer</u>.

88 + 56 = ...   144 – 56 = ...   144 – 88 = ...

Write down 3 sums that are related to each of these.

72 + 11 = 83, so ...., ... and ....

23 + 65 = 88, so ...., ... and ....

Mental Strategies

Look for Related Sums

A. 173 + 25
B. 20 + 56
C. 103 – 53
D. 198 – 173
E. 25 + 198

Bernard has to take an arithmetic test. He can't add up or take away, but he does know that 25 + 173 = 198. Which questions should he be able to answer?

....

Given that 238 + 156 = 394, do these in your head.

156 + 238 = ...   394 – 156 = ...   394 – 238 = ...

Use 359 + 162 = 521 to work these out:

521 – 359 = ...   162 + 359 = ...   521 – 162 = ...

Do the first sum, then fill in the rest of the gaps.

222 + 151 = ... – 151 = ... – 222 = ...

Sort these into 3 groups of related sums.

45 + 121 = 166   214 – 169 = 45   169 – 27 = 142

45 + 169 = 214   166 – 121 = 45   169 – 142 = 27

214 – 45 = 169   142 + 27 = 169   166 – 45 = 121

....

....

....

Add up your brothers and sisters — that's a related sum...

If a question looks really hard, there might be an __easier__ way to do it. If you can turn one sum into a __related__ sum, you might not have to actually work anything out.

Calculations — *Adding Numbers in Columns*

Before you <u>add 3-digit numbers</u> you have to <u>line up</u> the <u>hundreds, tens and units</u> — you'll end up in a real mess if you don't bother.

Adding 3-digit Numbers in Columns

EXAMPLE: What is 312 + 256?

First of all, write the numbers on <u>top</u> of each other with the digits <u>lined up</u>, like this.

```
  3 1 2
+ 2 5 6
```

Then add up the <u>ones column</u> (that's these bits).

```
  3 1 2
+ 2 5 6
      8
```

Write the answer here.

Next, do the <u>tens column</u>.

```
  3 1 2
+ 2 5 6
    6 8
```

Write the answer here.

To finish it off, <u>add up</u> the <u>hundreds</u> column.

```
  3 1 2
+ 2 5 6
  5 6 8
```

That's it. So the answer's 568.

```
  4 2 2        4 1 3        4 3 0        4 1 0
+ 2 6 6      + 2 2 4      +   4 5      + 3 2 5

..........    ..........    ..........    ..........

  4 1 6        4 1 4        4 1 3        3 1 2
+ 2 6 1      +   5 4      + 4 8 5      + 2 7 5

..........    ..........    ..........    ..........
```

Dick wants to become a professional disco dancer when he's older. To qualify for the Junior School of Performance Disco he needed to be able to work out 424 + 54 (this sum forms the basis of many cool disco routines).

He got an answer of 678. Was he right or wrong?

```
    ..........
  +
    ..........
```

.... So he was ....

Adding Numbers in Columns

If any <u>column</u> adds up to <u>ten or more</u>, you have to "<u>carry</u>" a bit to the next column.

EXAMPLE: Work out 238 + 354.

Start off just the <u>same</u> — write the numbers down, above each other.

```
  2 3 8
+ 3 5 4
_____
```

But when you add up 8 and 4, you get 12.

```
  2 3 8
+ 3 5 4
_____
      2
```
1

Put the 2 here, like before...

...but put the 1 under here, in the <u>next column</u>.

We say the 1 has been <u>carried</u>.

Carry the 1.

When you add up the next column, add the 1 <u>as well</u>.

```
  2 3 8
+ 3 5 4
_____
    9 2
      1
```

To finish it off, <u>add up</u> the <u>hundreds</u> column.

```
  2 3 8
+ 3 5 4
_____
  5 9 2
      1
```

That's it.
So the answer's 592.

Try this little lot and remember you sometimes have to carry.

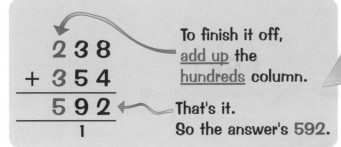

```
  4 1 7
+   2 4
_____

.............
```

```
  4 6 0
+   4 5
_____

.............
```

```
  4 1 0
+ 7 2 5
_____

.............
```

```
  4 6 6
+ 2 6 6
_____

.............
```

```
  4 1 5
+ 6 5 6
_____

.............
```

```
  4 1 8
+ 8 8 5
_____

.............
```

```
  8 7 7
+ 2 7 5
_____

.............
```

I carried 236 horses across the river in the morning and 456 in the afternoon. How many horses did I carry across the river in the entire day.

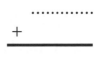

```
     ............
+
_____

  ...............
```

Stop CARRYING on — you've got SUM stuff to do...

Always add up the units first (right column), then the tens (middle column) and then the hundreds (left column). If a column adds to 10 or more, carry to the next column.

Calculations | # Subtracting Numbers in Columns

Things are starting to get tricky now. For these subtractions, you need to borrow when the number on the top is smaller than the number on the bottom.

Subtract Numbers by Borrowing

EXAMPLE: What is 835 – 96?

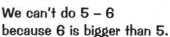

No I said borrowing, not burrowing.

Write the numbers with the units lined up.

```
    8 3 5
  –   9 6
  _____
```

Split the numbers into hundreds, tens and units.

```
  =   800 + 30 + 5
  –          90 + 6
      _____
```

EEK!
We can't do 5 – 6 because 6 is bigger than 5.

But we can BORROW a ten from the 30 to make 15. So we get 15 – 6 = 9. Borrowing ten means that 30 drops to 20.

```
  =   800 + 20 + 15
  –          90 +  6
      _____
                   9
```

The idea is always to subtract units first, then tens and then the hundreds.

EEK!
We can't do 20 – 90 either, but the 20 can BORROW a hundred from 800.

So we get 120 – 90 = 30
and 700 – 0 = 700

```
  =   700 + 120 + 15
  –           90 +  6
      _____
      700 +  30 +   9
```
= **739**

Add them up to get the final answer.

Now try these ones. Remember you'll have to borrow.

```
    2 1 4            200 + 10 + 4          100 + 110 + 4
  –   5 3     ➡    –       50 + 3    ➡   –        50 + 3
  _____          _____          _____

  ..........       ..............        ..............  = ........
```

```
    8 3 7
  –   7 9     ➡    ..............   ➡   ..............
  _____          _____         _____

  ..........       ..............        ..............  = ........
```

```
    5 3 6
  – 1 8 2     ➡    ..............   ➡   ..............
  _____          _____         _____

  ..........       ..............        ..............  = ........
```

Subtracting Numbers in Columns

On this page, I'll show you a different way to set out the example from the previous page.

A different way of *Setting It Out...*

EXAMPLE:

```
  H T U
  8 3 5
-   9 6
_____
```

SUBTRACT THE UNITS

We can't do 5 – 6, so we borrow from the tens column.

5 becomes 15, and the 3 in the tens column drops to 2

```
    2
  8 ⃥3 ¹5
-   9 6
_____
      9
```

15 – 6 = 9

You always take away the UNITS first, then the TENS and then the HUNDREDS.

SUBTRACT THE TENS

We can't do 2 – 9, so we need to borrow from the hundreds column.

The 2 in the tens column becomes 12, and the 8 in the hundreds column drops to 7

```
  7 ¹2
  ⃥8 ⃥3 ¹5
-   9 6
_____
    3 9
```

Now 12 – 9 = 3

SUBTRACT THE HUNDREDS

Easy: 7 – 0 = 7

```
  7 ¹2
  ⃥8 ⃥3 ¹5
-   9 6
_____
  7 3 9
```

Once you can follow the example, have a go at these:

```
  7
2 ⃥8 ¹2
-  5 6
_____
      6
```

```
4 3 5
-  2 9
_____
```

```
3 6 3
-  7 3
_____
```

```
4 5 1
-2 6 2
_____
```

Borrowing — now that's a subtract I like to talk about...

There's quite a lot to take in here. The examples on these two pages are the same — they're just set out differently. Keep reading through them until you can follow them.

Real Life Money Problems

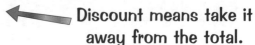

Money and maths questions go together like sherbet and liquorice
— so get stuck into these:

A mouse suit costs £42 to hire for a day. A tree suit costs £129.
If you hire both of them at the same time you get a £16 discount.

> How much does it cost to hire both suits?

← Discount means take it
away from the total.

The cost of both suits without the discount = __£42__ + __£129__ = __£171__

The cost of both suits with the discount = ... – .... = ...

 Due to custard damage, a mouse suit now
costs £34 and the discount has gone up to £25.

> How much does it cost to hire both suits now?

The cost without the discount = ... + ... = ...

The total cost with the discount = ... – .... = ...

The great composer, Johann Sebastian Froggatt, has a simple formula for calculating
the royalties owed to him by his record company. He multiplies £10 by the number
of CDs sold, and then takes away £20.

> Last year he sold 25 CDs. How much money did he earn last year?

£10 × __25__ = __£250__ , __£250__ – __£20__ = __£230__

So Johann Sebastian Froggatt earned __£230__ last year.

> So far this year he has sold 28 CDs. How much money has he earned this year?

£10 × .... = ... , ... – .... = ...

So Johann Sebastian Froggatt has earned .... this year.

> If he sold 11 CDs next year, how much would he earn?

....

....

He would earn .... next year.

Real Life Money Problems

1 pot of Froggatt's Banana Gravy costs 45p, and 1 battered fish costs £1.85. Mr I. Brow has £5. Will this be enough for him to buy 1 battered fish and 4 pots of Froggatt's Banana Gravy?

But I don't like banana gravy.

4 pots of Froggatt's Banana Gravy cost .... × 4 = ...

4 pots and 1 battered fish cost .... + ... = ...

If he can afford them, put a big tick in the box.

How much would 5 pots of banana gravy and 4 battered fish cost?

....

....

To keep up with the latest developments in hand-held technology, Big Bob bought 2 smiley puppets and 1 moody puppet. Smiley puppets cost £1.29 each and moody puppets cost £1.49.

How much change did Big Bob get from a £5 note?

....

....

....

Big Bob had £30 on Sunday. He spent half of it on Monday and then half of what was left on Tuesday.

How much did Big Bob have left?

TUESDAY

....

....

Solving Problems

Making Decisions and...

Check if the sums on this whole page are right.

If you add <u>2 even numbers</u> together you get an <u>even</u> number <u>answer</u>.

This one's wrong, because of this.

Put a cross in the box if you think the sum is wrong. And draw a line to the reason why it's wrong.

42 + 142 = 183 ✗   32 + 54 = 77 ☐

74 + 184 = 263 ☐   68 + 858 = 953 ☐   456 + 546 = 981 ☐

143 + 531 = 677 ☐

If you add <u>2 odd numbers</u> together you get an <u>even</u> number <u>answer</u>.

453 + 143 = 653 ✗   63 + 99 = 183 ☐   643 + 531 = 955 ☐

If you add an <u>odd</u> and an <u>even</u> number together you get an <u>odd</u> number.

84 + 77 = 154 ☐

245 + 38 = 342 ☐   482 + 845 = 934 ☐   42 + 99 = 134 ✗

Ace fighter pilot Dick Parsnip covered 43 enemy planes in custard last week. The other pilots from the Broughton Elite Squadron covered 49 planes with custard. Enemy sources claim the squadron covered a total of 93 planes with custard.

Could all these figures be right?

....

....

Yeah, you may have guessed that all the sums on this page are wrong — but it is picking the reason that's the tricky bit.

MATHS CLASSBOOK **4B**

...Checking Results

You can <u>check hard sums</u> by doing <u>easy ones</u> — just watch this.

John has calculated that 304 + 564 = 712. Is he right?

It's easy to do a rough check.
304 is close to 300 and 564 is close to 550.
Now 300 + 550 = 850, but 712 is nowhere
near 850 — so John is obviously wrong.

Actually, 304 + 564 = 868.

Do a rough check to see if these additions are right.

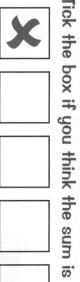

Tick the box if you think the sum is right.

204 + 642 = 748. Rough check: ..... *200* ..... + ... *650* ..... = ... *850* ..... ✗

392 + 478 = 785. Rough check: .... + ... = ...

194 + 798 = 823. Rough check: .... + ... = ...

634 + 632 = 1522. Rough check: .... + ... = ...

577 + 245 = 456. Rough check: .... + ... = ...

Tony and Bony are twins. Tony has won 263 prizes
for his mini-teacher pies. Bony has won 564. Their
dad reckons that they have won 727 between them.

Is their dad right?

.... + ... = ...

....

Fractions of Measurements

Get the hang of this example and you'll have no trouble with these 2 pages — honest...

> What is a tenth of 10 litres of rainwater?
>
> A tenth means that you have to divide by 10.
> 10 litres ÷ 10 = 1 litre.
> So, a tenth of 10 litres is 1 litre — simple.

What is half of 10 litres of rainwater?

....

Half of 10 litres of rainwater is ....

A fifth means divide by 5.

What is a fifth of 20 litres of rainwater?

....

A fifth of 20 litres of rainwater is ....

What is a quarter of 24 litres of fox and orange juice?

....

A quarter of 24 litres of fox and orange juice is ....

FOX AND ORANGE JUICE

What is half of 20 centimetres of ribbon?

....

Half of 20 centimetres of ribbon is ....

No foxes were harmed in the making of this page.

What is a twentieth of 40 metres of teacher-wrapping ribbon?

....

A twentieth of 40 metres of teacher-wrapping ribbon is ....

Fractions of Measurements

What is a third of 15 kilograms of cabbage?

A third means that you have to divide by 3.
15 kilograms ÷ 3 = 5 kilograms.
So, a third of 15 kilograms is 5 kilograms.

What is a tenth of 150 kilograms of cabbage? Tick the correct box.

10 kilograms		15 kilograms		20 kilograms	

What is a quarter of 100 kilograms of cabbage? Tick the correct box.

20 kilograms		50 kilograms		25 kilograms	

What is a fifth of 400 kilograms of cabbage? Tick the correct box.

80 kilograms		90 kilograms		40 kilograms	

David keeps 350 kilograms of plastic-coated cucumbers in his 7 office cupboards. There is the same weight of cucumbers in each cupboard.

What is the weight of cucumbers in each cupboard?

 Put your working here

....

There are .... kilograms of cucumbers in each of David's cupboards.

Laura has got her head stuck in a bucket. In the bucket there is some yellow slime that weighs 25 kilograms. In order to get her head out Laura will have to eat a fifth of the slime.

What does a fifth of the slime weigh?

....

A fifth of the slime weighs ....

Using fractions in real life — it's a dividing issue...

If you don't know what to divide by, write the fraction in symbols — so a twentieth would be $\frac{1}{20}$. Now you just have to divide by the number on the bottom, which here is 20.

Measures, Shape and Space

Finding Areas of Shapes

The Area of a Shape tells you How Big it is

This purple shape has a bigger area than the green shape — it's made of 7 squares instead of 6.

Both shapes are made of squares with sides 1 cm long. These are <u>SQUARE CENTIMETRES</u>. We measure the area of most shapes by saying how many square centimetres they take up.

I've got one. Leg it!

We'd say, "The green shape has an area of 6 square centimetres (6 cm²)" and, "The purple shape has an area of 7 square centimetres (7 cm²)."

This is how you write it — the little 2 means squared.

How many centimetre squares are there in these shapes?

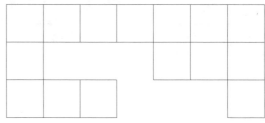

15 .... centimetre squares

.... centimetre squares

<u>Colour</u> the squares in as you <u>count</u> them — that way you won't add any in twice.

What are the areas of these shapes in cm²?

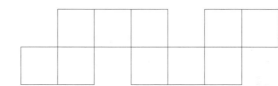

.... cm²

.... cm²

Shapes don't have to be the same to have the same area.

Oh, area. Not a rear?

All but one of these shapes have the same area. Circle the odd one out.

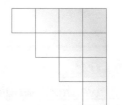

Split them into squares like the first one, then count how many squares each shape is made up of.

Finding Areas of Shapes

Areas of some more *Interesting Shapes*

We can roughly work out the area of Sam Croak's lily pad on this picture by counting roughly <u>whole square centimetres</u>, and then counting bits which are roughly <u>half square centimetres</u>.

Whole square centimetres:
<u>about 17</u>
Half square centimetres:
<u>about 6</u>
6 halves makes <u>**3 wholes**</u>.
So the area of the lily pad is roughly 17 + 3 = 20 cm^2.

Work out the area of each of these bog standard designs. Assume that each square is 1cm^2

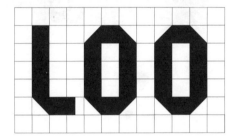

.... centimetre squares

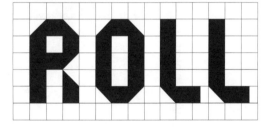

.... centimetre squares

Poor Supercod has been steamrolled by his arch-enemy Dr Eel.
Dr Eel has used his flattened remains to make tiles for his new bathroom.

By counting tiles and half tiles, estimate flattened Supercod's area (including his cape). Each tile is one square metre (1m^2).

Area of flattened Supercod is
.... m^2

I need a BATTER estimate for the area — COD you help...

A good way to find the area of strange shapes like flattened fish is to count full centimetre squares and then add on bits which are roughly half. It's not exact, but it's pretty good.

Giving Positions on Grids

These <u>grids</u> are a great way of describing where things are — you've just got to get the numbers in the <u>right order</u>.

Go <u>Across</u> then <u>Up</u> to find the <u>Position</u>

Now where did I put Major...

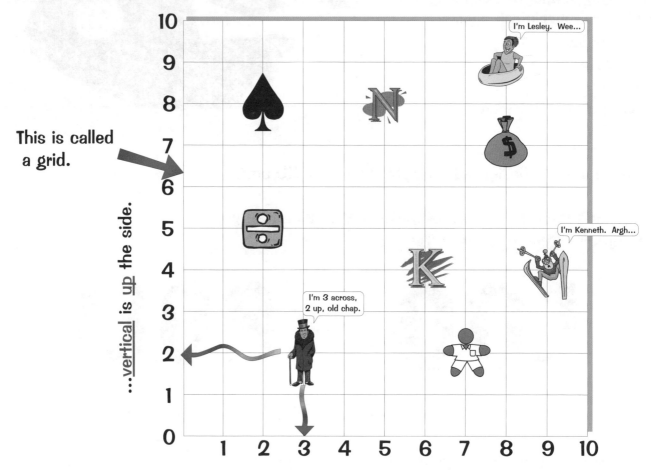

Horizontal is <u>across</u> the bottom...

EXAMPLE: The position of <u>Major Froggatt</u>, the great tycoon, is <u>3 across and 2 up</u>.

Describe the position of the letter K.

.... across and .... up.

Describe the position of the money bag.

.... across and .... up.

Who is at 8 across and 9 up?

.... is at 8 across and 9 up.

Describe the position of the ÷ symbol.

.... across and .... up.

Describe the position of the letter N.

.... across and .... up.

Who is at 9 across and 4 up?

.... is at 9 across and 4 up.

Giving Positions on Grids

There's a Short Way of Giving the Position

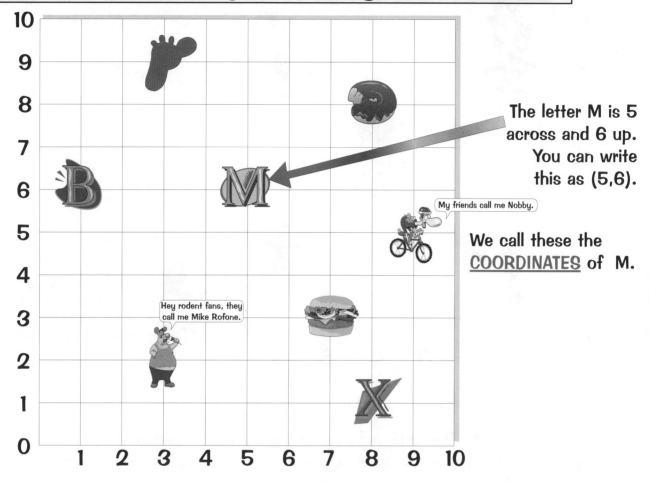

The letter M is 5 across and 6 up. You can write this as (5,6).

My friends call me Nobby.

We call these the COORDINATES of M.

Hey rodent fans, they call me Mike Rofone.

So instead of saying that the letter M is at <u>5 across and 6 up</u>, you can say it's coordinates are (<u>5,6</u>).

What is the position of the letter B?	What is the position of the Hamburger?
The letter B is at (........, ...).	The hamburger is at (........, ...).

What is the position of the purple foot?	What is the position of the letter X?
The purple foot is at (........, ...).	The letter X is at (........, ...).

Who is at (3,2)?	Who is at (9,5)?
.... is at (3,2).	.... is at (9,5).

I don't like Coordinates — I want Grid of them...

The easiest way to give positions from a grid is just to put the two numbers inside a bracket with a comma in between. Remember the first number is how many across, the second is how many up. And we call them coordinates.

Compass Directions

The direction between <u>north and west</u> is called <u>north-west</u> — who'd have thought it.

Never eat soggy wheat.

Mr Mexico's rhyme will help you remember the order of the points of the compass — North, East, South, West.

What is the direction of Mr France from Mr Portugal?

Start at Mr Portugal and <u>draw an arrow</u> to Mr France. Next <u>look</u> at the <u>compass</u> to see which direction the arrow matches — here it's <u>NE</u>.

What is the direction of Mr Switzerland from Mr Poland?

Mr Switzerland is .... of Mr Poland.

What is the direction of Mr France from Mr Poland?

Mr France is .... of Mr Poland.

Who is north of Mr Portugal?

Mr .... is north of Mr Portugal.

Who is south-east of the man at (4, 4), and what are his coordinates?

Mr .... is south-east of the man at (4,4).

His coordinates are (........,........).

Howdy, I'm from the West.

Draw an arrow in pencil on the grid and then match it to one on the compass.

Angles

Angles Measure how much Something Turns

Angles tell you how much something has turned. The bigger the angle, the bigger the turn. Turns are measured in <u>degrees</u> — you need to know the 3 most common ones.

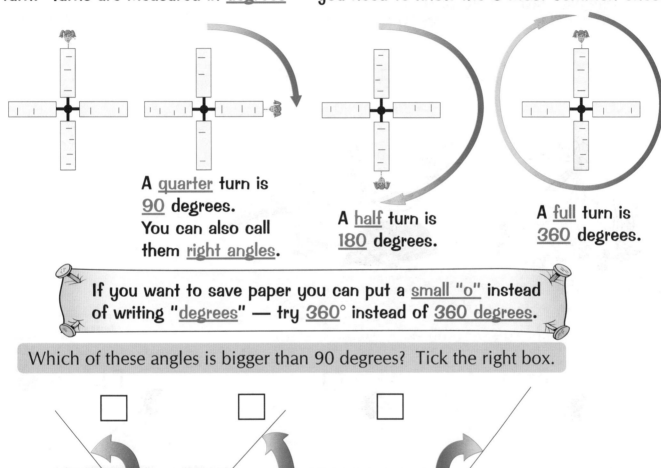

A <u>quarter</u> turn is **90** degrees.
You can also call them <u>right angles</u>.

A <u>half</u> turn is **180** degrees.

A <u>full</u> turn is **360** degrees.

If you want to save paper you can put a <u>small "o"</u> instead of writing "<u>degrees</u>" — try <u>360°</u> instead of <u>360 degrees</u>.

Which of these angles is bigger than 90 degrees? Tick the right box.

Which of these angles is bigger than 180°?

Circle the person (or worm) whose book is open at an angle of 180°.
Draw a square around the one whose book is open at an angle less than 90°.

Using Set Squares

Use Set Squares to draw Angles

There are two kinds of set squares.
One has angles of 90°, 60° and 30°.
The other has angles of 90°, 45° and 45°.

Using a set square, measure the angles of the mouths of these birds.

1 ....

2 ....

3 ....

4 ....

Johnny has three attempts at throwing the javelin.
The ideal angle is about 45°.
Tick the box next to his best throw.

I'd use a set square to measure these.

Draw these angles using a set square.

a) 90°   b) 30°   c) 45°   d) 60°

Put these angles in order of size. Start with the smallest first.

60°, right angle, 45°, 100° ....

Straight line, 85°, 90°, 160° ....

33°, 90°, 100°, straight line ....

Remember how many degrees are in a right angle and a straight line.

Tricky Angle Stuff

Some *Tricky Turning* Problems

The hour hand on a clock turns through a quarter turn from 3 o'clock to 6 o'clock. That's 90° in 3 hours. So it turns <u>30° in 1 hour.</u>

Describe in degrees the movements of the hour hand on a clock if the time changes from:

Just remember — it turns 30° each hour.

1 o'clock to 4 o'clock ....

10 o'clock to 2 o'clock ....

6 o'clock to 12 o'clock ....

2 o'clock to 8 o'clock ....

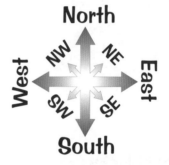

If you turn from north to north-east, you're turning through <u>half a right angle</u>. A right angle is 90°, so north to north-east is half of this which is <u>45°</u>.

All these changes in direction are making me dizzy!

In what direction will you face if you turn:

90° clockwise from facing East? ....

45° anticlockwise from facing South-west? ....

135° clockwise from facing North? ....

Stig is a wild chef. He prefers to cook his food by electrocution.

Clockwise, how many degrees will he have to turn the dial to cook:

Wild Boar? ....

Giant Rat? ....

Ostrich? ....

You turn through 3 positions in a half turn which is 180°. So work out how many degrees to turn through 1 position.

This is a turn up for the books...

For these questions, the trick is to find how many degrees you turn between each position. For a clock it's 30° per hour. Work this out first, then it's dead easy.

Solving Problems

Making Shapes

This is great — a chance to cut up bits of paper instead of doing sums.

Cutting and Folding to make new Shapes

What you do is <u>fold</u> a piece of paper over a couple of times,
so you can make <u>more than one cut</u> with <u>one snip</u> of the scissors.

EXAMPLE:

Start off with this <u>dead boring</u> sheet of paper.

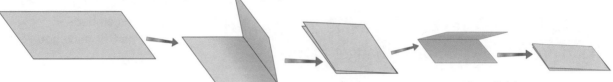

<u>Fold</u> it over to get a
rectangle half the size.

Then <u>fold</u> it over again.

Now you're ready to start the
<u>cutting</u>. Make one cut like
this:

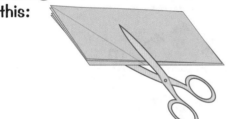

<u>Unfold</u> it, and you
get a <u>hexagon</u> like
this:

Now have a go at these.

I've folded a piece of paper once — draw on the piece below
where I should cut to get a diamond shape when I unfold it.

I said <u>fold</u> the paper,
not <u>chew</u> the paper!

Make <u>two</u> cuts in this...

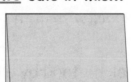

...to get <u>this</u>

This one's a bit harder. I've folded the paper over twice —
I want to make one cut to get four triangles when I unfold it.
Mark on the paper below where I should cut it.

Cut this <u>once</u>...

...to get <u>this</u>

Once you've worked these out,
get some paper and <u>try it</u>.

Perimeter and Area

The Perimeter is the Distance Around a Shape

The perimeter is found by adding together the lengths of the sides of a shape.

EXAMPLE:

Find the perimeter of the rectangle below:

6 cm

4 cm

> Add together double the length and double the width.

Double the length: $6 \times 2 = 12$

Then double the width: $4 \times 2 = 8$

Add the two together to get the perimeter:

$12 + 8 = 20$

So the perimeter is 20 cm.

The Area is Length Times Width

What is the area of a 5 cm by 6 cm rectangle?

....

....

And what's the area of an 8 cm by 4 cm rectangle?

....

....

> Finding the area is dead easy. Just multiply the length by the width

Mr MacNutter has to have a square plate so he can have neat food.
He won't be happy unless he has has 225 cm² of bacon rashers.

15 cm

15 cm

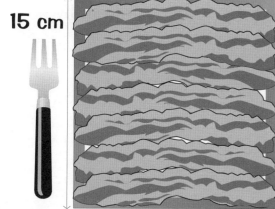

Length = ... cm

Width = ... cm

Length × Width =

.... × .... = ... cm²

Is Mr MacNutter happy with his plate?

....

Multiples of 2, 3, 4, 5 and 10

Multiples of 2 and 4 are *Always Even*

The "Multiples of 2" are all the "even" numbers.

They all end in 0, 2, 4, 6, or 8.

Have a look at these numbers, then circle all the multiples of 2.

16	86	23	44
8	11	17	22	33

This time, circle the multiples of 4.

16   86   23   44

8   11   17   22   33

Multiples of 4 are all even too, but not all even numbers are multiples of 4. Have a look at the ones you've circled already, to see which divide by 4.

Any *Multiple of 10* is a *Multiple of 5*

Which of these are multiples of 10?

Multiples of 10 end in 0.

25   15   24

30   32

17   93

50   40

Which are multiples of 5?

....

All the multiples of 10 are also multiples of 5 — so you can write those down straight away. Now look for anything that ends in 5.

If it's a *Multiple of 3*, the Sum of its digits *will Divide by 3*

Which of these are multiples of 3?

63   The sum of the digits is _6+3 = 9_ which _does_ divide by 3.
So 63 _is_ a multiple of 3.

52   The sum of the digits is _____ which _____ divide by 3.
So 52 _____ a multiple of 3.

123   The sum of the digits is _____ which _____ divide by 3.
So 123 _____ a multiple of 3.

Recognising Multiples

There are 4 Main tests to Learn

1) If it ends in 0, 2, 4, 6, or 8, it's a <u>multiple of 2</u>.
2) If the sum of the digits divides by 3, it's a <u>multiple of 3</u>.
3) If it ends in 0 or 5, it's a <u>multiple of 5</u>.
4) If it ends in 0, it's a <u>multiple of 10</u>.

Circle the multiples of 2 in black and the multiples of 5 in blue.
Underline multiples of 3 in black and multiples of 10 in blue.

25   20   27   225
    18   50   32

Work out whether these are multiples of 2, 3, 5 or 10.

28 is a multiple of ....

30 is a multiple of ....

12 is a multiple of ....

100 is a multiple of ....

50 is a multiple of ....

Even if you find it's a multiple of 2, you <u>still need to check</u> the others — it might be a multiple of <u>more than one</u> number.

Alan has 141 space rockets. He wants to share them out equally either between his 2 brothers <u>or</u> his 3 cousins <u>or</u> his 5 nephews.

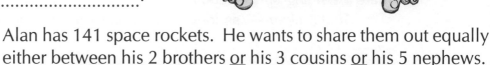

Find out whether Alan should give his space rockets to his brothers, his cousins or his nephews.

That's a roundabout way of asking whether <u>141 is a multiple of 2, 3 or 5</u>.

141 .... a multiple of 2.

141 .... a multiple of 3.

141 .... a multiple of 5.

So Alan can only share his rockets equally between his ....

Multi pulls? Bell ringers are good at them...

Multiples do look yukky. But they're alright really. A multiple of 5 is just a number in the 5 times table. There's loads of tricks here for spotting certain ones quickly. If you learn them, it'll help you lots with these questions.

Reasoning About Numbers

Explain How You Solve Problems in Your Head

You should be able to do <u>simple sums</u> in your head — without writing anything down. But when you work out a sum in your head, you still have to <u>think</u> about it.

You probably do the sum <u>bit by bit</u> to make it easier. I know I do. This page is about <u>explaining</u> what goes on in your head when you think about sums.

EXAMPLES:

32 + 18 = 50

<u>Explanation</u>: First I added the 2 to the 18 to make 20. Then I added the 30 to the 20 to make 50.

107 + 250 = 357

<u>Explanation</u>: There are three hundreds and fifty and seven. That makes 357.

32 x 2 = 64

<u>Explanation</u>: 32 x 2 is 32 + 32. 30 + 30 is 60, and 2 + 2 is 4. 60 + 4 is 64.

Those were the ways I think about these sums.
There's nothing <u>special</u> about them — you might have <u>different ways</u>.
That's okay — as long as you can <u>explain</u> how you do it.

Answer these sums and explain how you did them.

41 + 39 = ... Explanation: ....

....

202 + 190 = ... Explanation: ....

....

60 – 29 = ... Explanation: ....

....

26 x 2 = ... Explanation: ....

....

Reasoning About Numbers

Here's some more sums for you to do in your head and explain how you did them.

600 – 170 = ... Explanation: ....

....

55 × 2 = ... Explanation: ....

....

23 + 37 = ... Explanation: ....

....

Explain How You Solve Problems On Paper

Sums that are <u>more difficult</u> can't be done in your head.
Unless you're <u>really clever</u>, it's easier to do them <u>on paper</u>.
But it's still important to be able to <u>explain</u> how you do it.

EXAMPLE: <u>453 + 169</u>. That's a bit too tricky to do in my head, so I'll <u>write things down</u> first.

<u>Explanation</u>: 169 is 100 + 60 + 9. Add them one at a time. 453 + 100 is 553. 553 + 60 is 613. And 613 + 9 is 622. <u>Answer: 622</u>.

Explain how you work out these sums, and give your answer.

396 + 153. Explanation: ....

.... Answer: ....

245 + 331. Explanation: ....

.... Answer: ....

624 + 181. Explanation: ....

.... Answer: ....

487 + 103. Explanation: ....

.... Answer: ....

Calculations

Division with Money

In real life, you sometimes have to <u>divide</u> up amounts of <u>money</u>.
It's really not that hard. Work it out in <u>pence</u> — then <u>convert back to pounds</u>.

Dividing Money — use a Decimal Point

EXAMPLE: Hank came joint first in Scunthorpe's annual one-handed bean-juggling contest. He had to share the £4 prize money with 9 other people.

How much money did Hank get?

There were 10 people altogether, so you have to divide £4 by 10.

It's easiest if you write the £4 in pence first — 400p.

Now, <u>400 ÷ 10 = 40</u>, so the answer is £0.40. ← This is just another way of writing 40p.

Now see if you can do these ones yourself:

What is £2 divided by 4?

What is £1 divided by 10? ← Turn the £1 into £1.00, then do the division.

....

£1 divided by 10 is £........·..........

£2 divided by 4 is £........·..........

What is £5 divided by 2?

What is £4 divided by 5?

....

....

£4 divided by 5 is £........·..........

£5 divided by 2 is £........·..........

Rob designs posters for marrow festivals. He was paid £10 for 4 of them. How much did he get per poster?

....

£.............. divided by .... is £........·..........

MARROW MANIA
...the marrowfest to end all marrowfests.

We'll show you a gourd time

All the marrow you can munch — and more!

Sponsored by Marrow-in-Furness District Courgette

Money problems? Decimals will point the way...

Money problems really aren't that bad. All you have to remember is work it out in <u>pence</u>, then convert to pounds. If everything's in pence, you just do it like a normal sum.

Rounding After Division

Sometimes an answer has to be a <u>whole</u> number.
If you get a remainder, you have to <u>round the answer off</u>.

Round Off *if you need a whole number*

I have some boxes and 30 cakes ready for the Cardiff Cake-balancing Contest. If each box can hold 4 cakes, how many boxes can I fill?

30 ÷ 4 = 7 remainder 2. This means that 7 boxes will be full of cakes and 2 cakes will be left over. So I can only fill 7 boxes completely.

Rounding <u>down</u> means you <u>ignore the remainder</u>.

If a clog-box holds 6 clogs, what is the least number of boxes I need to store 13 clogs?

Rounding <u>up</u> means you <u>add 1</u> to the answer.

13 ÷ 6 = 2 remainder 1, so if I had only 2 boxes I'd have a clog left over. That means I need 3 boxes to hold all 13 clogs.

See if you can do these — you'll have to round either up or down:

Pru has 45 crowns and loads of boxes. Each box can hold 7 crowns. How many boxes can she completely fill with crowns?

....

Pru will be able to fill .... boxes completely.

Donald gives Pru 3 roses every day. He has 17 roses left. How many more days will he be able to give Pru 3 roses?

....

Donald will be able to give Pru 3 roses for another .... days.

A super-large box holds 12 bottles of Froggatt's Sprout Shampoo. Pru has 57 bottles messing up her bathroom.

What is the least number of boxes that she will need to store them all?

....

Number of boxes needed is ....

| Calculations | # Fractions and Division |

Divide by 2 for a Half, Divide by 4 for a Quarter

Fractions have a lot in common with division.
When you divide something, you end up with a fraction of it.

This is Micky, the chef with the big moustache.
He's baked a giant spinach and blueberry cake.

If I asked Micky to divide the cake by two and give me one of the pieces, how much cake would he give me?

Put a tick under the right amount of cake.

....

If I asked Micky to give me half the cake, how much cake would he give me?

   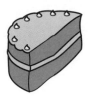

It's the same amount.
Dividing by 2 is the same as halving.

....

If I asked him to divide the cake by 4 and give me a piece, how much would I get?

Mmmm... spinach and blueberry cake

      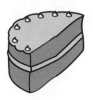

....

And if I asked him to give me a quarter of the cake, how much would I get?

Again it's the same as the one above.
Dividing by 4 is the same as quartering.

....

Fractions and Division

A Quarter is a Half of a Half

If you <u>halve a half</u>, you get a <u>quarter</u>. You might have noticed this already. Have <u>another look</u> at those pieces of Micky's spinach and blueberry cake.

Cut this cake in half, and what do you get? Put a tick under the right one.

 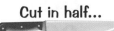 

....

Now here's half a cake — cut it in half and what do you get?

 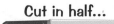 

....

Cut a quarter of a whole cake and what do you get?

....

Cut something in <u>half</u>, then cut it in half <u>again</u>, and it's the same as cutting a <u>quarter</u>.

Do these sums to work out a quarter.

Half of 240 is ___120___ and half of ___120___ is ___60___, so a quarter of 240 is ___60___.

Half of 100 is .... and half of .... is ...., so a quarter of 100 is ....

Half of 160 is .... and half of .... is ...., so a quarter of 160 is ....

Half of 400 is .... and half of .... is ...., so a quarter of 400 is ....

Doing Division On Paper

Short Division

One way of doing division sums is to take away multiples that you already know.
Keep on doing this until you get to zero. Then see how many multiples you've taken away.

EXAMPLE:

96 ÷ 6 is written like this ──────────▶ 6)96

Now think of a multiple of 6 that you know.
60 is 10 × 6. That's a good one to start with. ──▶ − 60

Take away the 60 and you're left with 36. ──────▶ 36

Now let's take away another multiple of 6.
36 is 6 × 6. So we can take that away too. ──▶ − 36

And we're left with nothing. That's the aim. ──▶ 0

Note down how
many lots of 6 you
are taking away.

10 × 6

6 × 6

16

Now, we've taken away ten lots of 6.
And then we've taken away another six lots of 6.
Add them up. 10 + 6 = 16, so we've taken away 16 lots of 6.

And that's your answer — 96 ÷ 6 = 16.

Keep taking away multiples you know to get the answer to these division sums.

5)95
−50   10 × 5
45
−45   9 × 5
0
Answer: 19

7)98

Answer: ....

4)92

Answer: ....

6)78

Answer: ....

8)120

Answer: ....

7)119

Answer: ....

Money and Fraction Problems

Fractions of Money and Real Life Things

You'll often be asked to find a <u>fraction</u> of something in <u>real life</u>.
Remember — that's often just a simple <u>division</u> sum.

EXAMPLE:

Mark won a free 10-day holiday in Tahiti.
He also gets <u>21 free drinks</u> from the bar.
He's already had a <u>third</u> of them.
How many free drinks is that?

ANSWER: you need to find <u>a third of 21</u>.
A third is the same as <u>dividing by three</u>.
21 ÷ 3 = 7. So Mark has had <u>7 drinks</u>.

For a <u>half</u>, divide by <u>2</u>.
For a <u>third</u>, divide by <u>3</u>.
For a <u>quarter</u>, divide by <u>4</u>.
For a <u>fifth</u>, divide by <u>5</u>.
For a <u>tenth</u>, divide by <u>10</u>.

Answer these questions about fractions by doing simple division sums.

Mark also took his children for a tenth of the normal price.
The normal price was £1500 for all of them. How much did Mark pay?

....

Mark's daughters, Sarah and June, have a
"pointy sand thing" competition with two
local boys. They build a sand thing that's
80 cm high. The boys' one is only half as
big. How big is the boys' pointy sand thing?

....

Sarah wants to buy a multicoloured beach ball. Mark agrees to
pay for three quarters of it if Sarah pays for a quarter from her
pocket money. The beach ball costs £2.

How much does Sarah pay? .... And how much does Mark pay? ....

Mark meets Mikado, the famous two headed nose flute player.
They meet after a fifth of Mark's 10-day holiday. After how many days is that?

....

Mark offers to pay a third of Mikado's air fare so he can
visit him back home in Britain. The air fare is £600.
How much would Mark pay?

....

Mental Calculation

Split into Tens and Units to Double or Halve

A good way to double numbers is to split them up into tens and units. Double the tens, and double the units. Then add them back together again.

So to double 36, split it into tens and units....

Double them both...

Then add the pieces back together again.

$$36$$
$$30 \qquad 6$$
$$60 \qquad 12$$
$$72$$

Double these numbers by splitting them into tens and units:

45 is __40__ + __5__ so double 45 is __80__ + __10__ = __90__

38 is .... + ... so double 38 is .... + ... = ...

27 is .... + ... so double 27 is .... + ... = ...

47 is .... + ... so double 47 is .... + ... = ...

You can halve numbers in exactly the same way. Split them up into tens and units, halve them both, then add them back together again.

So to halve 72, split it into tens and units....

Halve them both...

Then add the pieces back together again.

$$72$$
$$70 \qquad 2$$
$$35 \qquad 1$$
$$36$$

Halve these numbers by splitting them into tens and units:

46 is __40__ + __6__ so half 46 is __20__ + __3__ = __23__

82 is .... + ... so half 82 is .... + ... = ...

78 is .... + ... so half 78 is .... + ... = ...

96 is .... + ... so half 96 is .... + ... = ...

Mental Calculation

Doubling Numbers in Your Head

You'll often get
questions that ask you
to <u>double a number</u>.

It's a good idea to know
them so well you can
do it <u>in your head</u>.

Doubling numbers with <u>0</u> or <u>00</u>
on the end looks pretty tricky.
But it's <u>easy</u> when you know how.
Simply do it <u>without</u> the 0s —
then <u>stick them back on</u> again.
Double 38 is 76. Double 380 is 760.
Double 3800 is 7600.

Write down the doubles of these numbers:

Double 34 is ....   Double 320 is ....   Double 4600 is ....

Double 14 is ....   Double 430 is ....   Double 1200 is ....

Double 21 is ....   Double 280 is ....   Double 3300 is ....

Double 48 is ....   Double 190 is ....   Double 4400 is ....

Double 29 is ....   Double 350 is ....   Double 2500 is ....

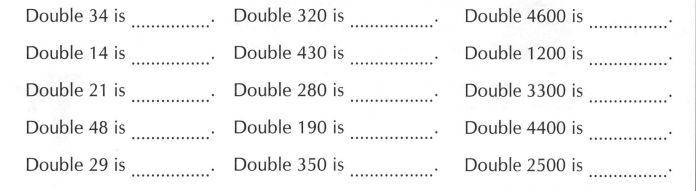

Here's something else you need to know.
Doubling is the <u>opposite of halving</u>.

Doubling and halving
must be opposites
because
<u>multiplication is the</u>
<u>opposite of division</u>.
Doubling is × **2**, and
halving is ÷ **2**.

Double 18 is 36 — so half 36 is ....

Double 420 is 840 — so half 840 is ....

Double 900 is 1800 — so half 1800 is ....

Work out these halves:

Half 34 is ....   Half 420 is ....   Half 8000 is ....

Half 64 is ....   Half 720 is ....   Half 7400 is ....

Half 98 is ....   Half 680 is ....   Half 5600 is ....

Half 22 is ....   Half 260 is ....   Half 2800 is ....

Half 86 is ....   Half 500 is ....   Half 6200 is ....

Checking Answers

Use Subtraction to Check Addition

What subtraction could you use to check these additions?

The best way to <u>check an addition</u>, is to <u>take</u> one of the numbers you added away <u>from the answer</u>.

To check 63 + 25 = 88, use _88 – 25_ . The answer should be _63_ .

To check 281 + 114 = 395, use .... The answer should be ....

To check 53 + 74 = 127, use .... The answer should be ....

Now write down a different subtraction that you could use for each of the sums above.

_88 – 63 = 25_

It <u>doesn't matter</u> which number you take away — so long as you get back to the <u>other number</u>.

....

....

Check these subtractions with an addition.

94 – 22 = 72   ....

357 – 123 = 234   ....

468 – 251 = 217   ....

Make sure it's the number you <u>took off</u> that you <u>add</u> back on.

Some of these answers are wrong.
Do a check to see which ones are wrong.

218 – 105 = 213   _213 + 105 = 318_   _The answer is wrong._

135 + 23 = 158   ....

363 – 333 = 36   ....

Maurice has Christmas presents for 127 friends. He can deliver 103 presents himself but will have to send the rest by post.

How many presents does Maurice have to post?

....

Now check your calculation.

....

Checking Answers

Use Division to Check Multiplication

Check these by doing a division:

$15 \times 4 = 60$ *60 ÷ 4 = 15, so the answer is right.*

$25 \times 2 = 50$ ....

$50 \times 5 = 500$ ....

$40 \times 4 = 1600$ ....

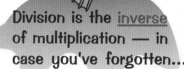

Division is the <u>inverse</u> of multiplication — in case you've forgotten...

...and multiplication is the <u>inverse</u> of division, wow.

Check these by multiplying:

$800 \div 2 = 300$ ....

$900 \div 3 = 300$ ....

$730 \div 2 = 365$ ....

$240 \div 4 = 60$ ....

Check these by doing the inverse.   **Just look at the <u>sign</u> — then do the <u>opposite</u>.**

$20 \times 7 = 170$ ....

$180 \div 2 = 90$ ....

$180 \div 3 = 80$ ....

$150 \times 2 = 300$ ....

Bertie went fishing on Saturday. He caught 280 fish, which he shared between his 2 good friends, Sydney and Stanley.

How many fish did Stanley get?   ....

Check your answer by doing the inverse.   ....

Look for a sign and do the opposite — but not on the roads...

<u>Times</u> and <u>divide</u> are <u>opposites</u>. So if you divide by a number and then multiply by the same number, you'll always get back to the number you started with.

Fractions and Decimals

"1 out of 2" is the Same as "2 out of 4"

Have a look at this set of tiles.

There are different ways you can
say how many of them are red.

How many tiles are there in total? ....

How many tiles are red? ....

So .... out of .... tiles are red.

How many tiles are in each row? ....

How many red tiles are in each row? .... in every .... tiles are red.

Both those ways of saying it are the same, so that means:

" .... out of .... " tiles and " .... in every .... " tiles must mean the same thing.

How many days do you go to school each week? ....

Once you know <u>how many</u> days you go to school in <u>1 week</u>, you can work out how
many days you go in 2, 3, 4... weeks — just <u>multiply</u> by the number of weeks.

How many days do you go to school in 3 weeks? .... days

What about in 5 weeks? .... days   6 weeks? .... days

If Paul gets a free breadcrumb
for every 2 trees he climbs,
how many trees does he have
to climb to get 3 breadcrumbs?

I get <u>1 breadcrumb for every 2 trees</u>, so
that's 2 breadcrumbs for 4 trees. You just
<u>multiply</u> the number of trees by the number
of breadcrumbs I get for each tree.

.... trees

Fractions and Decimals

Convert these measurements from centimetres to metres.

There's just one thing you need to know, so <u>learn it</u>:

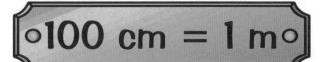
○100 cm = 1 m○

673 cm = ...*6.73*.... m

281 cm = ... m

496 cm = ... m   562 cm = ... m   744 cm = ... m

All you're really doing is <u>dividing by 100</u>.

Write these amounts again in £s.

○ 100p = £1 ○

279p = ...*£2.79*....   300p = ...

545p = ...   614p = ...

889p = ...   708p = ...

Work out these lengths:

First change all your measurements into <u>centimetres</u> — they're <u>whole numbers</u>, which are much easier to work with.

3 m – 25 cm = ...*300*... – ...*25*... = *275 cm*

Don't forget to put the <u>units</u> in your answer — you've been working in <u>centimetres</u> so just add "<u>cm</u>".

5 m + 30 cm = ... + ... = ...

8 m – 50 cm = ... – .... = ...

Ernest is the greatest musician in Bugsville. By playing his music he earned 42p on Monday, £3.05 on Tuesday, 53p on Friday and £5.68 on Saturday.

How much did Ernest earn during the whole week?

<u>First</u> add up the amounts for Monday and Tuesday, <u>then</u> add on Friday, <u>then</u> Saturday — that way you won't get confused.

42p + £3.05 = ... p + ... p = ...p

.... + 53p = ... p + ... p = ...p

.... + £5.68 = ... p + ... p = ...p

Give your final <u>answer in £s</u> if it's <u>more than 100p</u>.   = £ ....

| Calculations | ## Halving and Doubling |

Add a Number to Itself to Double It

Double these numbers by adding each one to itself.

"Doubling" just means "Multiplying by 2" — but it's easier to say.

Double 10 = *10 × 2* = *10 + 10* = *20*

Double 20 = ... = ... = ...

Doubling 10s is pretty easy — you can ignore the zero while you're doubling, then stick it back on at the end.

Double 30 = ... = ... = ...

Double 40 = ... = ... = ...

Double 50 = ... = ... = ...

See if you can double these in your head.

Stick your thumb over the last zero and you'll see the numbers you've already doubled. Now just write down their double then pop the zero back on the end — piece of cake.

Double 100 = *200*

Double 200 = ...   Double 400 = ...

Double 300 = ...   Double 500 = ...

Split Numbers Up to help you Double Them

Split these numbers into tens and units — then just double both and add them up.

Double 25 = *double 20 and double 5* = *40 + 10* = *50*

Double 15 = ... = ... = ...

Double 45 = ... = ... = ...

Double 26 = ... = ... = ...

Double these in your head.   Double 11 = ...

Double 150 = ...   Double 250 = ...

Don't forget the 2 tricks — 1) ignore the zero while you double the rest, or 2) split the number into two easier doubles.

Double 35 = ...   Double 55 = ...

Halving and Doubling

"Halving" is the Opposite of "Doubling"

Halve these numbers by looking for addition doubles.

Instead of multiplying by 2, you're <u>dividing by 2</u>.

100 = ...*50 + 50*..., which is ...*double 50*..., so ...*50*... is half of 100.

80 = ..., which is ...., so .... is half of 80.

40 = ..., which is ...., so .... is half of 40.

200 = ..., which is ...., so .... is half of 200.

500 = ..., which is ...., so .... is half of 500.

Split these numbers up to help you halve them.

Which came first — doubling or halving...

It's a good idea to <u>split these up</u> into two numbers — 24 is 20+4, so that's double 10 <u>plus</u> double 2.

24 is ...*double 10 and double 2*..., and ...*10 + 2 = 12*..., so ...*12*... is half of 24.

46 is ...., and ...., so .... is half of 46.

32 is ...., and ...., so .... is half of 32.

64 is ...., and ...., so .... is half of 64.

Halve all these in your head.

You might be able to halve these straight away — otherwise <u>split them up</u>.

Half 90 = ...   Half 30 = ...   Half 18 = ...

Halving's <u>not quite like</u> doubling — <u>you can't</u> always ignore the last zero and then stick it back on the answer.

Half 140 = ...   Half 800 = ...

Half 88 = ...   Half 360 = ...

Write these numbers as a double and as a half.

<u>Halve</u> the number to find the double, and <u>double it</u> to find the half — sounds a bit backwards...

22 is double ...*11*... and half ...*44*... .

50 is double .... and half ....   42 is double .... and half ....

Try these sums — you're bound to HALVE a good time...

Splitting numbers into tens and units makes loads of sums much easier. It works for bigger numbers too — just split the hundreds or thousands up as well.

Calculations	# Addition Doubles

99+1, 98+2... They all Add Up to 100

There are loads of pairs of numbers that add up to 100.
Use this simple method to find them all:

4-Step Method

1) Start with "99+1=100".
2) Take 1 away from the 99 and add it onto the 1 — that gives you "98+2=100".
3) To find new pairs, keep taking 1 away from the first number and adding 1 to the second number.
4) When you get to "50+50=100", stop — you've found them all.

Write down the first 4 pairs of numbers that add up to 100.

99 + 1 = 100

....

....

....

....

Fill in the gaps to find pairs that add up to 100.

Take the number away from 100 to find the missing number.

90 + __10__ = 100   .... + 13 = 100   65 + ... = 100

75 + ... = 100   .... + 24 = 100   .... + 37 = 100

62 + ... = 100   .... + 89 = 100   11 + ... = 100

Pairs that Add Up to 1000

Which of these pairs make 1000?

The ones that end in 00 are pretty easy to add up — I'd check those first if I were you.

500 + 500 ✓   150 + 950 ☐   350 + 650 ☐

450 + 450 ☐   450 + 550 ☐   400 + 600 ☐

600 + 400 ☐   300 + 800 ☐   250 + 750 ☐

Fill in the gaps to find pairs that add up to 1000.

Just take the number away from 1000 to find the missing number.

900 + ... = 1000   .... + 850 = 1000

950 + ... = 1000   .... + 200 = 1000

Adding Repeated Numbers

Always Look for *Repeated Numbers*

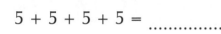

See how quickly you can add these up.

$5 + 5 + 5 + 5 =$ .... | OK, <u>4 lots of 5</u>. That's pretty easy — it's just **4×5**. This <u>next</u> one is <u>still 4×5</u>, but with two more numbers added on.

$5 + 5 + 54 + 5 + 12 + 5 =$ *4x5 plus 54 and 12* = *20+54+12* = *86*

$3 + 3 + 15 + 32 + 3 + 3 =$ .... = ... = ...

$2 + 2 + 2 + 50 + 12 + 2 =$ .... = ... = ...

If you're really lucky, there might be a <u>couple of numbers</u> that are repeated.

$2 + 2 + 2 + 10 + 10 + 10 =$ .... = ... = ...

$5 + 5 + 5 + 3 + 3 + 5 =$ .... = ... = ...

Look for *Nearly-Repeated Numbers*

Add these up as quickly as you can. | If you can find a **3**, a **4** and a **5**, that's <u>nearly as good</u> as finding three **4s** — they both add up to the <u>same amount</u>.

$4 + 3 + 5 + 4 + 4 + 4 =$ *6 x 4* = *20*

$9 + 11 + 10 + 10 + 10 =$ .... = ...

$5 + 5 + 6 + 4 + 5 =$ .... = ...

OK, all these are <u>5×</u> <u>whatever</u> — but you still need to work out <u>which</u> number to <u>multiply</u>.

$3 + 2 + 3 + 4 + 3 =$ .... = ...

Reginald has recently moved to Transylvania and joined the local library. He wants to take out 3 copies of the book "Bloodsucking for Beginners", 1 copy of "Bat-Keeping for Busy People", 2 copies of "Dressing to Kill" and 2 copies of "Surprise Birthday Cakes".

Help Reg work out the total number of books by looking for "repeated numbers" and "nearly repeated numbers".

....

Adding Decimals

The word "decimals" sounds really scary, but believe me, they're not.
Try writing down an amount of money, like £2 .30 — there, you've written down a decimal.

Line up the Decimal Points to Add Decimals

Add £2.30 and £4.52.

$$\begin{array}{r} £2.30 \\ + £4.52 \\ \hline £6.82 \end{array}$$

1) Decimals are just like normal numbers.

2) All you need to remember is to line up the decimal points at the beginning.

3) Then add the numbers as if the decimal point wasn't there.

Once the decimal points are lined up, add the numbers column by column, starting on the right.

0+2=2

3+5=8

2+4=6

Hurry up — I can't hold you much longer...

So, £2.30 + £4.52 = £6.82.

Add these up, by lining up the decimal points.

£5.60 + £4.25 = £ ....

£1.40 + £1.35 =

$$\begin{array}{r} £1.40 \\ + £1.35 \\ \hline \quad . \quad \end{array}$$

£ ....

+ _____
  _____

+ _____
  _____

3.20 + 6.70 =

....

+ _____
  _____

2.80 + 6.15 =

....

Even if there's no £ sign, they're still decimals — so line up the decimal point and add the numbers a column at a time.

Subtracting Decimals

Subtracting decimals is almost as easy as adding them.
Make sure the decimal points are lined up, then just take them away as usual. But remember...

Always Take the Smaller Number
from the Bigger Number

Do these subtractions by first lining up the decimal points.

The first number is the biggest — put that on top.
Put the other number right underneath, with the points carefully lined up — then take it away...

£5.90 – £3.60

= £ ....

$$\begin{array}{r} £5.90 \\ -£3.60 \\ \hline . \\ \hline \end{array}$$

£6.45 – £2.33

= £ ....

£8.24 – £1.12

= £ ....

This next one isn't about money — but it's just the same really... Imagine there is a £ sign if it makes it easier.

9.55 – 5.40

= ....

Percival pays £3.90 for his lovely new sofa. He has a voucher worth £2.40 and pays the rest in cash.

How much cash does he pay for his new sofa?

Just take the smallest amount away from the biggest — exactly like you've done for all the other questions.

£ ....

Estimating Times

If you haven't got a stopwatch, you can always estimate how long things take.

Choose Your Units Carefully

1) Decide whether it takes seconds, minutes, hours, days, weeks, months, years...
2) Then guess how many days, weeks or whatever.

Do you spend seconds, minutes or hours on these each day?

getting dressed ......*minutes*.........

clothes-shopping ....

brushing your teeth ....

Now estimate how long you spend eating breakfast, sleeping and sneezing.

Nobody's going to check up on you, so just have a rough guess.

eating breakfast ....

sleeping ....

sneezing ....

Estimate how long it takes to:

make some toast ....

travel to school ....

eat a sandwich ....

count to 100 ....

read this page backwards ....

If you've got no idea — find out. Most of these you could do and time yourself.

Estimate how long it will take you to cross the playground. ....

Now do it! Time yourself or get a friend to time you.

....

Timetables and Calendars

Reading Timetables

Not that sort of timetable...

Have a look at this timetable to see what time the train leaves Millom.

Easy — just look for <u>Millom</u>, and read off the time below.

Millom	Foxfield	Askam	Barrow
9.00	9.05	9.15	9.30

The train leaves Millom at ....

What time does the train leave Askam? ....

How long does it take to travel from Millom to Barrow?

<u>First</u>, you need to find out <u>what time</u> the train leaves <u>Millom</u> and what time it arrives in <u>Barrow</u>.

The train leaves Millom at ...., and arrives in Barrow at ....

It takes .... minutes to travel from Millom to Barrow.

Now work out the <u>difference</u> between the two times.

How long does it take to travel from Askam to Barrow?

It takes .... minutes to travel from Askam to Barrow.

I'm not too early, am I...

Reading Calendars

This calendar only gives you the first letter of each day of the week — <u>S</u>unday, <u>M</u>onday, <u>T</u>uesday, <u>W</u>ednesday, <u>T</u>hursday, <u>F</u>riday, <u>S</u>aturday.

Which day of the week is 17th November 2000?

Look for the <u>number 17</u> — then <u>draw a line</u> straight up, to see which day it is.

....

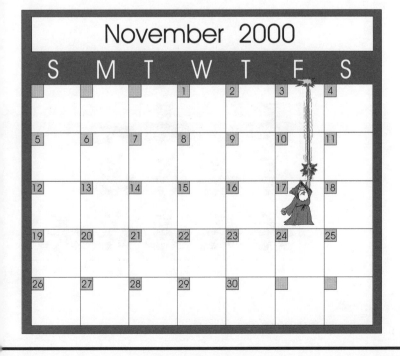

November 2000

S	M	T	W	T	F	S
			1	2	3	4
5	6	7	8	9	10	11
12	13	14	15	16	17	18
19	20	21	22	23	24	25
26	27	28	29	30		

How many days are there in November 2000?

....

What day of the week is the last day in November 2000?

.... 30th November

Pictograms

Reading Pictograms

This pictogram shows how many times 6 friends visit the bathroom each day.

1 toilet roll means 2 trips to the bathroom — so half a toilet roll must be 1 trip to the bathroom...

= 2 trips to the bathroom

Bertie　Billie　Sarah　Denise　Wilbert　Amanda

How many times a day does Billie visit the bathroom?

6 times

How many times a day does Amanda visit the bathroom? ....

What about Wilbert? ....

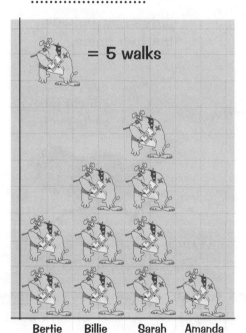

= 5 walks

Bertie　Billie　Sarah　Amanda

Bertie, Billie, Sarah and Amanda all have pet dogs. The pictogram shows how many times each of them walks their dog in a month.

How many times a month does Amanda walk her dog? ....

What about Sarah? ....

Billie? ....

The pictogram on the right shows the number of cars parked in the school car park during one week.

 = 20 cars

How many cars were parked on Monday? ....

How many cars were parked on Thursday? ....

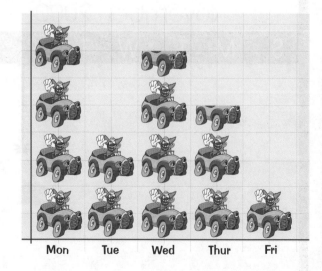

Mon　Tue　Wed　Thur　Fri

Pictograms

Drawing Pictograms

Month	Tally	Frequency
January	ЦЦ ЦЦ	10
February	ЦЦ |||	8
March	ЦЦ	5
April	||	2
May	||||	4
June	ЦЦ ||||	9

This tally chart shows how many times Sue tripped over her shoelaces in 6 months.

Draw a pictogram to show the data.

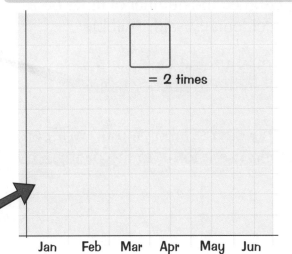

☐ = 2 times

Jan   Feb   Mar   Apr   May   Jun

Pick a symbol to represent <u>Sue tripping twice</u> — it can be anything, like a <u>shoe</u> maybe...

She tripped up <u>10 times in January</u> — so you'll need to draw <u>10 ÷ 2 = 5</u> shoes here.

Arnie, Barbie and Colin are comparing their collections of earwigs.

Choose a symbol to represent 5 earwigs.

☐ = 5 earwigs

	Number of earwigs
Arnie	20
Barbie	40
Colin	0

Use your symbol to draw a pictogram of the data here.

Now draw a pictogram with each symbol representing 10 earwigs.

☐ = 10 earwigs

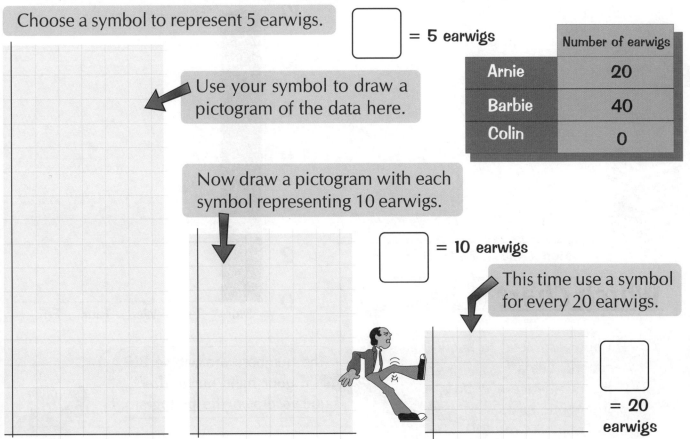

This time use a symbol for every 20 earwigs.

☐ = 20 earwigs

Each name starts with a <u>different letter</u> — so you could use that letter to <u>label each column</u>.

Pictograms? — I prefer kilograms myself...

Always make your pictures really simple in pictograms — that way they won't take long to draw. They don't have to be perfect — but make sure they're the <u>right size</u>.

Choosing Charts

3 Charts to Learn

Last week, Bernard the librarian counted the number of times he accidentally said, "wibble".

Count up the tallies and fill in the <u>frequency table</u>.

	Tally	Frequency
Monday	IIIII IIIII II	*12*
Tuesday	IIIII IIIII IIII	
Wednesday	IIIII IIIII	
Thursday	IIIII IIIII	
Friday	IIIII IIIII III	

Choose a symbol and draw it here, then use it to fill in the <u>pictogram</u> below.

☐ = 2 wibbles.

Now finish this <u>bar chart</u> showing the same data:

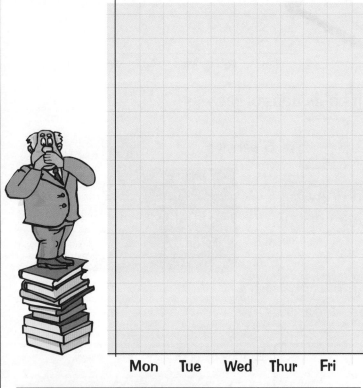

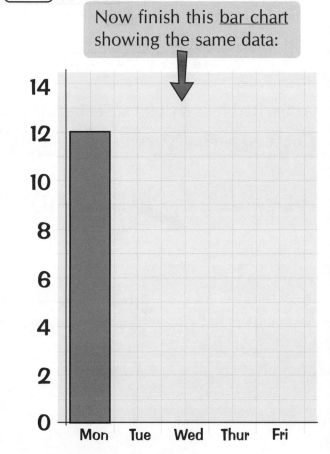

Which Chart is Best?...

1) If you really need to know the numbers, use a <u>frequency table</u>.
2) If the numbers are SMALL, a <u>pictogram</u> is best.
3) If the numbers are BIG, use a <u>bar chart</u>, unless...

The numbers are wibble BIG if your hand hurts after you've drawn the pictogram.

4) ...they're MULTIPLES of 50 or 100 — then a <u>pictogram</u> might be better.

Which chart is best for the "wibble" data?   ....

Index

Index